THE HILLS BEYOND

THOMAS WOLFE

THE HILLS
BEYOND

With a Note on Thomas Wolfe by
EDWARD C. ASWELL

PERENNIAL LIBRARY
Harper & Row, Publishers
NEW YORK, EVANSTON, AND LONDON

THE HILLS BEYOND was originally published by Harper & Brothers in 1941.

First PERENNIAL LIBRARY edition published 1964 by Harper & Row, Publishers, Incorporated, New York, Evanston, and London.

LIBRARY OF CONGRESS CATALOG CARD NUMBER: 41-21548

M-O

Contents

THE HILLS BEYOND

CHAPTER I

The Quick and the Dead

About midway along the Atlantic seaboard of the North American continent lies a strip of land which is known today as the State of Old Catawba. It is an ancient part of the everlasting earth, but its history is quite young. One of the earliest references to it occurs in the chronicle of old Hugh Fortescue. His narrative is so well known that it would hardly bear recounting, were it not for the curious legend which has grown out of it.

In the month of September, 1593, Fortescue, one of the hardiest and most celebrated sea adventurers of the time, set sail from Plymouth harbor with a full cargo of provisions and material, and, in addition to his crew, a company of one hundred and seven men, women, and children, whom he proposed to land upon the shores of Old Catawba to establish a colony there. The colony, as everyone knows, was founded four months later, in January, 1594. According to Fortescue's account, he remained for two months, helping the colonists build huts and log houses; then Fortescue sailed for England, leaving the colony apparently well established, with everything going briskly.

It was the old sea dog's intention, as he tells us in his lusty chronicle, to return again early the following year with additional supplies for the settlers, and with the further purpose, of course, of collecting and taking home the first fruits of their crops or findings in the

1

New World. Troubles at home, however, delayed him
far beyond his reckoning, and it was August, 1595,
before he stood in past the shifting dunes again, into
the pearl gray waters of the Great Sound. He was a
good six months late. And everyone knows what he
found.

The settlement was still there, but all the people
had disappeared. The natural supposition was that they
had been massacred by the Indians. Curiously, however,
the rude huts and cabins were intact. Fortescue says
that they had been stripped of every utensil, ornament,
and stick of furniture that might conceivably be of use
to anyone, but there was no evidence of violence. The
whole place was just empty and deserted. And, nailed
to a tree at the edge of the clearing, was a kind of rude
sign on which had been crudely painted the word
"here"—or "heare," as it was actually spelled. Below,
an arrowhead, blazed in the bark, pointed toward the
wilderness. This was all.

Fortescue and his men, taking this clue for what it
was worth, or what it might imply, explored the wilderness of the whole region for weeks. They found nothing
—not even a footprint—that could give any hint of
what had happened to the people in the settlement. So,
after exhausting every hope and every possibility of
search, Fortescue set sail again and headed back for
England.

That's the story—all that was ever known. No new
light has since been shed upon the mystery. But the
human mind is so constructed that it cannot abide an
unresolved mystery. From Fortescue's day onward, people wondered what became of the Lost Colony, and
since history gave no answer, they were free to invent
an answer of their own. This, as we shall shortly see, is
exactly what they did.

Time passed, and other settlers came to Old Catawba. The manner of their coming was very much like
that by which all the colonies of the British Crown
were eventually peopled. And like the nation of which

it was to be a part, Old Catawba grew from east to west. Its expansion followed the inevitable direction prescribed by geography and economic pressure. The earliest settlements were in the tide-water regions along the coast. In the 1660's the population of the colony did not exceed ten thousand persons, and they were distributed in a thin belt of settlements that penetrated no more than seventy-five or a hundred miles inland.

One hundred years later, just before the outbreak of the Revolutionary War, the population had grown to two hundred thousand, and had pushed westward to the foothills of the upper Piedmont, at the base of the great mountain wall, three hundred and fifty miles from the ocean. Intrepid pioneers and daring huntsmen had actually surmounted the last barrier of the West, had blazed their way through the wilderness, had lived for months alone in what was then Indian country, and had returned at length laden with furs and skins and other trophies of the hunt, as token of the fact that they had been there. The first settlements behind the mountain wall, in the great wilderness of western Catawba, occurred in the years immediately following the Revolution, and as a direct result of the war: the settlers were men who had been soldiers in the Continental Army, and had been induced to go there through land grants given them as a reward for their services.

Slowly but surely the movement to the West continued, until by the first quarter of the nineteenth century the western regions of the state had so grown in numbers that they threatened to wrest control of the government from the East, which had hitherto maintained its supremacy unchallenged. The West demanded its rightful representation in the legislature. The East, stiffnecked with pride, refused, and since the East still had the edge in population, as well as most of the wealth, the refusal stood. Thus began the first in the long series of conflicts between East and West that were to disturb the life of the state for years.

But it was an unequal struggle, and time was with the West. The East fought back desperately against this giant stripling, this obscure country cousin, this uncouth hillbilly, but the West, with gangling stride and dangling arms and gap-toothed grin, refused to know when it was licked, and instead just wiped the lank hair from its eyes, spat briefly through its bloody lips, and kept coming on again after every knockdown. The East used every weapon at its command, and when fair means failed, it did not scruple to use foul. One of the foulest and most specious weapons that it used was the arrogant claim that the East was superior to the West in birth and breeding, and therefore born to rule.

Now the history of genealogies is very significant and curious. In America, as in most young countries, people are much less likely to be snobs over the thing they have than over the thing they lack. Thus, Americans are seldom snobs about money, but they are often snobs about "family." The amount of time spent by certain people in New England and the South in talking about their "families" is appalling. In the South, particularly, this preoccupation seems to absorb most of the spare energies of the female population, for it is an axiom of Southern life that a woman without "family" is nothing. A woman may be poor; she may be abysmally ignorant (and usually is); she may have read nothing, seen nothing, gone nowhere; she may be lazy, nasty, vain, arrogant, venomous, and dishonest; her standards of morality, government, justice may not differ one whit from that of the lynching mob: but if she can assert, loudly and without challenge, that her "family" is older (and therefore better) than other families, then her position in the community is unquestioned, she is the delicate flower of "Southern culture," she must not be "talked back to"—she is, in short, "a lady."

So it was in this final phase of the war between the East and the West. As a last resort, the East claimed the right to rule the West on grounds of "family." In a state which had hitherto been singularly free of aristocratic pretensions this was a most peculiar development. But the reasons for it are not far to seek.

The East now knew that its cause was hopeless. It had grown fat on power, and now it saw that it must yield before the new men of the West. It read the signs of its declining influence, and hated to think of the future. So, as nearly always happens under such circumstances, the East took refuge in the glories of an imagined past as compensation for the threatened loss of its future.

What happened was this:

The bare facts of the Lost Colony, as old Hugh Fortescue recorded them, had been known for years to the more literate people in the eastern part of the state. The mystery surrounding the disappearance of those first colonists had always been a subject of speculation, and a body of legend had grown up about it. According to this legend, the people of that colony were not killed, but were taken captive and carried off into the wilderness by an Indian tribe. In the course of time they adopted the language and customs of their captors; they intermarried with the Indians and bore children; and these children, in turn, intermarried with colonists of a still later date. Thus the Lost Colony was not really lost at all. And it followed from the legend that the descendants of this colony were not only still living, but could lay claim to the oldest English ancestry of any people in the New World—dating thirteen years before Jamestown, and twenty-six before Plymouth.

For years, this legend had existed as folklore, kept alive by idle curiosity and gossip. No one believed it. It was not until about a decade before the Civil War, at a time when the legends of Massachusetts and Virginia were already venerable with tradition, that the Catawba legend began to congeal into a form imposing enough for anyone to take it seriously.

Then it was that a professor of history at one of the local colleges published a book entitled *The History of the Lost Colony*. It achieved some passing notice in the world at large, being generally received in learned circles as a fairly interesting experiment in conjectural possibility. The author himself did not make any greater claim for it. He was too conservative and cautious a historian to try to prove that the legend of the colonists' survival through intermarriage with the Indians was anything more than a theory of what *might* have happened. Still, in a manner that is distressingly familiar to the local historian everywhere, he sometimes let his patriotic ardor get the better of his scholarly judgment, and, in modern parlance, was inclined "to give himself the breaks."

No doubt it was for this reason that the book produced a considerable sensation at home. Its sales in Old Catawba were phenomenal, and its effect was both profound and startling, in a way that the worthy professor had never intended or foreseen. The time was ripe for it, and people in the eastern part of the state fell upon the book eagerly, and began straightway to embroider and to weave, as composers do, with what are called "improvisations on a theme." The ladies proved themselves especially proficient in this form of intellectual exercise. Starting from scratch—indeed, from the most scratchy sort of scratch—they began to erect a glittering edifice of pure fantasy, all of it proceeding, of course, out of something which started merely as a titillating thought, grew rapidly to a rosy hope, and ended in an unshakable conviction that *they themselves* were descended from the presumptive survivors of the Lost Colony.

In almost no time at all a new and highly exclusive social organization came into being, calling itself The Society of the Sons and Daughters of the Aborigines. The aristocratic pretensions of its members threatened overnight to eclipse even the haughty claims of the F.F.V.'s and the Mayflower descendants. The Sons and Daughters of the Aborigines had just discovered who they were, and from this point on they would play second fiddle to no one. No doubt it was all well enough, they said patronizingly, to talk about royal grants and tide-water plantations and the early days of Plymouth, but such trifling originalities as these could not be expected to matter very greatly to people who were *aboriginally* descended from the *first* English colonists *and* from Indian chieftains. It was quite surprising to see how proudly the Aborigines laid claim to this tinge of savage color in their veins. Ladies whose husbands would have reached for their dueling pistols at any imputation of a *recent* tinge of color in their blood felt no hesitation whatever in proclaiming their dusky ancestors of some two and a half centuries before.

There have been critics unkind enough to suggest that throughout this whole extraordinary performance necessity was the mother of invention, and that the ready acceptance of the Catawba legend as historic fact was no more than might have been expected of a people who had too long been irked by their own obscurity and too long been indifferent to the claims of "family." Thus, "a lady of family" in Virginia is known to have remarked one time, when informed that her nephew had married a mere nobody for no other reason than because he loved her: "Well, what else can you expect? He was brought up in Johnsville, and that's *practically* a Catawba town." This shrewd observation reflects pretty much the estimation in which Old Catawba has been commonly held by outsiders. And certainly it is true that the history of the state has always been more distinguished for its homespun ruggedness than for its aristocratic splendor.

In spite of all gibes and taunts, The Society of the Sons and Daughters of the Aborigines grew strong and flourished throughout the eastern part of the state. And what had begun as a social organization quickly became the chief ally of entrenched power in the state's politics. The Sons and Daughters brought up their heaviest artillery of "family" to stem the rising tide of the West, and in the pivotal campaign of 1858 they nominated one of their own number to run for Governor against a country lawyer from the wilds of Zebulon County.

The country lawyer stumped the state, pleading the cause of democracy, and telling his audiences that the ruling caste in the East, with its money and privileges

and humbug aristocracy, was dead and didn't know it.
Like Swift when he announced the death of Partridge,
the almanac maker, his logic was irrefutable: for, as Swift
retorted, when Partridge came forward to assert that he
was still alive, *if Partridge was not dead, he should have
been*—so the country lawyer held to the proposition
that the East was dead, or should be; and his delighted
followers called the fight that ensued "The Battle of the
Quick and the Dead."

Under that banner the East was beaten. The West
had won at last. And the leader and hero of that victory
became from that time on the symbol of the West.

His name was Zachariah Joyner—a name famous to
everyone who since that time has lived upon Catawba
earth and breathed Catawba air. Throughout his life he
was a vigorous and undaunted champion of the common people. The pretensions of the Aborigines dis-
gusted him, and he let no opportunity go by to flail
them with the brutal lash of his coarse but devastating
ridicule.

Joyner's opponent in the campaign for the governor-
ship was himself a Son of the Aborigines, his right to
this distinction being founded upon the aristocratic
claims of his mother, a charming lady who had inherited money and idleness, both together, and with this
endowment had thus been one of the first to trace her
ancestry back to the Lost Colony. Her son had cam-
paigned vigorously to save what he called "our precious
heritage" and "the Catawba way of life" from the raw
crudeness of a Western victory. In the end he was even
rash enough to accept Joyner's challenge to appear on
the same platform and debate the issues face to face.
On this occasion the gentleman-champion of the East
gave everything he had. He was not only eloquent in
his show of filial devotion to his mother—"that delicate flower of Southern womanhood, etc. . . . to
whom I owe, etc. . . . at whose knees I learned, etc."
—but he also sought to endear himself to the masses by
condescension: he went so far as to admit that he made
no claims to aristocratic lineage on his father's side, his

father's people being descended, so he said, "from good old yeoman stock."

"Good old yeoman stock, my ——!" bellowed Zachariah Joyner in rebuttal. "They came here because the jails in England were crowded, and to keep from being hanged"—this was an exaggerated reference to the settlement of a group of exiled convicts on the eastern coast in 1683—"and the only yeomen they ever saw were the yeomen of the guard!"

So Zachariah Joyner won, and his victory was a great deal more than the triumph of one half of the state over the other half. It was the triumph of the common man—of all the obscure and unknown lives that somewhere had turned a wheel, or swung an ax, or plowed a furrow, or blazed a trail and made a clearing in the wilderness. His was the voice, the tongue, the language of every one of these who had lived and died and gone unrecorded to the earth—and who now arose again, incarnate in one living man, to say to all proud hearts, stiff necks, and Aborigines soever that in the final reckoning the representatives of privilege must bow before the insistent rights of universal humanity.

Old Catawba had found its man.

CHAPTER II

Old Man of the Tribe

Zachariah Joyner was never one to indulge in the reverent pruning of family trees. When he was Governor of Old Catawba he often said that if people in the eastern part of the state would spend less time in thinking about where they came from, and more in thinking about where they were going, they would be a lot easier to get along with.

He was also impatient of all attempts to dignify himself and his own family genealogically. In the heyday of his later fame, the Aborigines made some conciliating overtures to bring Catawba's most distinguished citizen into the fold. They did not quite dare hint that Zack had as good a right as anybody else to claim an ancestor in the Lost Colony, for they knew too well what he would say to that; but they did draw up quite a formidable account of the doings of the Joyners in the annals of history. They traced the name back to the Middle Ages. They even had one of the Joyners doing valiant service in defense of King Richard of the Lion Heart, when that great sovereign was surrounded by a murderous host of Saracens before the walls of old Jerusalem. They dug out others with baronial titles, and found some of them contending back and forth in the Wars of the Roses. There were Joyners who had fought loyally under the banners of King Charles, and others just as doggedly with Cromwell's men. From that point the earliest migrations of the family were traced to Virginia, thence to the coastal regions of Catawba, and finally to their stronghold in the mountain districts of the West. By dint of much contriving, the whole thing had been linked together in a kind of chain.

But Zachariah was not impressed. His comment on the document, when it was presented for his inspection and approval, was characteristically blunt and to the point:

"I don't know where we came from, and, what's more, I don't give a damn. The point is, we're here now."

There was not only good democracy in this, but the ring of sound truth, too. For the essential trait of the Joyner tribe was in those words. They were "here now," and Catawba would have been inconceivable without them. They were, in fact, a kind of native dragon seed. They may have had some other and more ancient antecedents, but in their magnificent quality of Now-ness—the quality of being what they were because they were where they were—they were so naturally a part of western Catawba, its life, its speech, its history, even the clay of its soil, that any other previous existence for them seemed fantastically detached, ghostly, and unreal.

Since every mother's son of us has got to come from somewhere, their lineage, no doubt, went back like everyone's to Father Adam, or to the origins of primeval man. So perhaps their ancestor was some prehistoric anthropoid. But if anyone wants to know who the founder of the family was, the answer is that it was old William Joyner, the father of Zack, and the sire of the whole clan. Even today the memory of old William is still kept alive in the hills, for in his own way he attained a legendary repute which almost equals that of his more celebrated son.

There is some doubt about William Joyner's antecedents, and no certainty whatever about where he came from. It is known that he came to Zebulon County because of a Revolutionary land grant. And the date of his coming is established. It was in 1793 when he took up his grant upon the south fork of what is now known as the Thumb Toe River. If he was not actually the first settler in that region, he was among the first. From this time on, people began to come in rapidly, and when William Joyner married, in 1798, the wife he took was the daughter of another settler who had recently arrived in the mountains.

Her name was Martha Creasman, and by her he had a family of seven. She died at the birth of her last child. Later, William married a second time. By this wife he had fourteen or sixteen children—for there were so many of them, and their destinies were so diverse, that even their number has been disputed. But of these matters, with all the ramifications of kinship and heredity they imply, it is our purpose to speak later. Here we shall tell a little more of William Joyner.

There were, in the earlier years of the present century, old men alive who could remember him; for he lived to a great old age, and there were people who were children in the 1840's who had seen him and had heard the stories men told of him. Even at that time, a hundred years ago, he was an almost legendary figure. The stories of his great physical strength, for example, were prodigious, and yet apparently were founded in substantial fact.

He was said to have been, particularly in his earlier years, a man of a hot temper, who liked a fight. There is a story of his fight with a big blacksmith: a quarrel having broken out between them over the shoeing of a horse, the blacksmith brained him with an iron shoe and knocked him flat. As William started to get up again, bleeding and half conscious, the blacksmith came at him again, and Joyner hit him while still resting on one knee. The blow broke the blacksmith's ribs and caved in his side as one would crack a shell.

He was known in his own day to be a mighty hunter; and old men who remembered him used to tell of the time he "chased the dogs the whole way over into Tennessee, and was gone four days and nights, and never knowed how fer from home he was."

There is also the story of his fight with a grizzly bear: the bear charged him at close quarters and there was nothing left for him to do but fight. A searching party found him two days later, more dead than living —as they told it, "all chawed up," but with the carcass of the bear: "and in the fight he had bit the nose off that big b'ar and chawed off both his years, and that b'ar was so tored up hit was a caution."

Then there is the story of the time when he walked off with enough leather on his back to shoe a regiment. The brother of Joyner's first wife owned a kind of trading post or country store, and had besides a pound of savage and ferocious dogs. It was the storekeeper's boast that no one but himself could manage these fierce animals, and certainly no one else had ever attempted to. People generally were afraid of them, and gave them a wide berth. Their owner was so proud of their untamed ferocity that on one occasion, when he was talking of his dogs to a group of men who were in his store, he offered any man who could subdue them "as much leather as he can tote out of here upon his back."

William Joyner was present and instantly accepted the challenge. In spite of the efforts of his friends to dissuade him, he went out to the pound, and, while the others watched, opened the gate and went in. The great dogs sprang snarling at him with bared fangs. According to the story, "he jest snapped his fingers once or twice," and the dogs whimpered and came crawling to him like a pack of curs. To add insult to injury, he is said to have stooped down and picked up two of the largest and most savage of the dogs and held them under his arms, "a-hangin' thar real foolish-like, like a couple of pigs." After walking about the pen with them a time or two, he tossed them down, snapped his fingers again, opened the gate, and walked out unscathed.

The storekeeper, although beaten and dumbfounded,

was as good as his word. He pointed to the pile of leather in his store and told William he could take as much as he could carry. Joyner stood there while his companions heaped the leather on, and finally staggered out the door with eight hundred pounds of it on his shoulders.

There are many other stories about him, but these suffice to indicate the unusual qualities of his person, his great strength, and his undaunted courage. He was said by everyone who ever saw him to have been a person of remarkable gifts. Indeed, one does not have to probe a mystery to find an explanation for the amazing family he produced: the seed of all their talents was aware in him. Although he came to Zebulon with nothing but his rifle and his grant of land, within twenty years, through his ability as a shrewd trader, he had accumulated what was, in his time and place, a substantial property. He was the owner of a mill, to which his neighbors brought their corn for grinding. He increased his holdings until he owned and had under cultivation hundreds of acres of the most fertile land in the beautiful valley that now bears the name of Joyner's Creek. And eventually he became the owner of the largest and most flourishing trading post in the whole district.

From these beginnings came the start of the whole clan. It is true that Zachariah, in the later years of his political career, made frequent and eloquent reference, in the phrases of the orotund rhetoric of which he was a master, to "the little log cabin where I was born." It is further true that the little log cabin where Zachariah so often and so advantageously asserted he was born, still exists, kept piously by the State Historical Commission, in a condition of trimmed, sodded, planted, and be-flowered snugness that it assuredly did not know at the time when William Joyner lived in it. The State Highway Commission has likewise memorialized the sanctuary in a system of neat signs, which notify the modern pilgrim that he is now approaching "the birth-place of Zachariah Joyner—four miles."

It is unfortunate, perhaps, both for the lovers of

sentiment and the believers in historic fact, that Zachariah was not born here at all. William Joyner did live here for years, and built the cabin with his own hands, with the assistance of some friendly Cherokees; but by the time of Zachariah's birth, his father was already a person of considerable substance, and in accordance not only with his new position, but with the expansive needs of his growing family, he had built the larger and much more substantial dwelling that adjoins it, and which also still exists. "The little log cabin where I was born," existed in Zachariah's childhood as a kind of outside kitchen; it was certainly in such a capacity that Zachariah himself must have known it, no matter how he remembered it later in the more imaginative flights of political oratory by which he gave it fame.

In his later years, William Joyner having now become a man of weight and standing in the community, his wife tried, as wives of successful citizens are apt to do, to ameliorate some of his social imperfections. The story goes that she tried to get him to wear shoes in summertime—for apparently he was a man who liked bare feet, and when he went out to the fields to work, the weather and the season permitting, he always worked so.

Failing to win this really formidable concession, the worthy woman then attempted to persuade him "at least to put your shoes on when you come into the house." Her efforts even in this direction were not successful, for although he made some effort to please her, he "kept forgittin'." Failing in all this, she finally tried to prevail on him "for pity's sake, at least to put your shoes on when company comes." But this also proved too much, for she used to say despairingly: "I don't know what to do with him. I've begged an' I've pled an' he promises to try, but the minute we have company—even when the preacher's there—here he comes without his shoes, trampin' along out of the fields in his big feet."

As for "Bear" Joyner—for, after his famous encounter with the grizzly, he was known by this name—he would often say: "I thought I was marryin' me a wife, but I reckon what I done was to go an' git myself hitched to a blacksmith. My advice to you young'uns is, if you ever go and git yourself married, make sure first whether you're marryin' a woman who is goin' to cook fer you, or one who is goin' to try to throw you down an' shoe you every time you come into the house."

He was a man of keen wit, and everyone who ever knew him said that he would have "gone far" if he had had the advantages of formal education. He was unable to read or write his own name until he was more than forty years old; but he learned how to do both in his later years. Indeed, he developed quite a taste for reading, and, limited as his facilities were, he managed to acquire a surprising store of bookish information.

Bear Joyner, like his famous son, was increate with myth, because the very nature of the man persuaded it. Such myths, then—*facts* most probably, indeed—as his bear-fighting, hunting, blacksmith-crushing, dog-mastering, and his instinctive shoelessness we have adduced to give the flavor of the man.

These things get into the story, make the picture. Yet it is not the Myth that falsifies the true identity of man (our debunking truth-tellers of the present notwithstanding—would to God they were themselves debunked!). The Myth is true. Let those who doubt it deny that Lincoln liked a joke, and had a gift for making one; split rails; was very strong; said h—l and d—n; so far as we can guess, was not averse to—; was pungent in his speech, and said his legs were long enough to reach the ground (which certainly was high sense); picked up the dirty pig; was chased out of doors by his wife—yes, and even when embarrassed by the presence of surrounding ladies on a railroad platform, told a little boy who pointed to a certain word scrawled upon the wall by other little boys, that the thing it stood for was "a station, son . . . the name, son, of a certain station . . . a most important station . . . the station where more men get on and off than any other station in the world."

A myth, then, to like food and women, and to take a drink? . . . A myth to know the use of corncobs in the country? . . . To be able to say ——, and make a joke about it? . . . To be a lawyer, and have "a high and squeaky voice," and yet be able to speak *Gettysburg?*

O, little men, come, come!

Then why the Myth?

The Myth is founded on *extorted* fact: wrenched from the context of ten thousand days, and rutted roads, the desolations of lost voices long ago, the rheumy nostrils in the month of March, the winter howling in the oak, the superfetation of the dreary wait, the vacancy of unremembered hours.

For it is not a question of having faith, or lack of it. It is a simple fact of seeing. Seeing, we are saved. Half-seeing, we are worse than blind. And wrong.

It is important, then, to know that William Joyner "chawed the b'ar." But it is even more important to know that William Joyner was a man who learned to read a book.

It may be that some later period in the human history will dispense with the whole necessity of print, and that book-reading, book-writing, book-publishing, all the ramified accessories that have accumulated since old Gutenberg, will (through some system of psychophones, printoscopes, empathic waves, or type telepathies; or what more of the strange and unbelievable we can wot not of) be as prehistoric as the dinosaur. But in William Joyner's day the thing was known—not only known, but, aside from speech, the swiftest and most common way of all communication; and the point is that, illiterate as he was until his fortieth year, unread, unlettered, not even knowing the look of his own name in common script—he learned it!

Why?

We do not know; and cannot guess the reason except that men sought India once, and braved inhuman seas beyond the world's edge, in their scallop shells; and looked at one another with "a wild surmise." As for all other antecedents—possible Joyners in the Middle Ages, with the Roses, or King Charles—let others search them: all things must have their precincts, and our own are there, in Old Catawba, with Bear Joyner, in the hills of home.

Whatever seed produced him, or what kernel of his own unknown heritage, the man was "there"—and not only "chawed the b'ar," but learned to read a book. And of all the facts that can be evidenced, of all the traits that bind the clan of William Joyner's seed together, none is more strange than its respect for learning.

Where did it come from?

In the century since old Bear Joyner's time, there have been some thousands of his name who have been dwellers in these hills. Some have been mountain folk, bowed down by poverty, who never learned to write, or to construe in print, their names. Others have been half-literate. Others have had the rudiments of education. Still others have risen in the world to places of commercial eminence: some have been lawyers, doctors, business men; there has been a preacher here and there; there has been more, much more, than an average sprinkling of "radical thinkers"—"atheists and agnostics" (that is to say, people who would openly debate the divinity of Jesus Christ, or the existence of "the after-life"); others who had "radical notions" (people who would challenge the accepted standards of law and property: there was one such who ran for Congress on the ticket of Eugene Debs, and got eight votes—it was said, however, that his sons and brothers did not vote for him). In the mountain districts to this day the Joyners have the reputation of being "queer." The word is not used scornfully, for generally, no matter what their station, the Joyners are respected folk. But any variation from the norm in them does not astonish anyone: people have come to accept it casually and as a matter of expected fact. If a Joyner is an "atheist," an "agnostic," a "socialist," a "radical," it has come to be accepted because the Joyners are "queer" folk.

But again—why?

Boiled down to their essential element, all of these "eccentric" qualities which have, for a hundred years or more, caused their neighbors to accept the Joyners as belonging to their special type, and "queer," are nothing but the marks of an intensely heightened curiosity, a questioning, probing, debating, and examining intelligence that their neighbors did not have. There's the mystery—if mystery it be; indeed, the only mystery there is.

The Joyners have always been "individualists." But so are all mountain folk. Yet other mountain folk are individualistic more convenably. Most mountain folk are individuals within the narrow frame of a convention. True, they will go their own way, make their own law, "take nothing off any man"—but all of this follows a close code. They are clannish, suspicious of the strange, world-lost, mistrustful of the outer world—conformant, really, in their non-conforming. For even when they go their way and kill their man, they are unquestioning of the special law of their own world.

In this respect the Joyners were all different from their neighbors, and the pattern of divergence was set by the founder of the clan. At a time when it was the convention for all men in the wilderness to be illiterate, in a place where the knowledge contained in books was of no earthly use, nothing would suit old Bear Joyner but that he must learn to read.

At a later time, as has already been stated, the genealogists of the Aborigines tried to account for Zachariah Joyner's distinction by tracing his line back to the Middle Ages. It was no use. The answer lay closer home. For no one ever really knew where his father

came from. And it did not matter. Old Bear Joyner
came from the same place, and was of the same kind, as
all the other people in the mountains. But he was a
man who learned to read. And there is the core of the
whole mystery.

CHAPTER III

The Great Schism

If, as Carlyle says, the history of the world is recorded in
the lives of its great men, so, too, the spirit of a people
is recorded in the heroes it picks. No better illustration
of this fact could be found than in the life of Zachariah
Joyner. Historically, his position is secure enough. True,
his greatest fame is where he would himself have
wished it to be—at home. His name has not attained
the national celebrity of a Webster or Calhoun; no
doubt most people outside Catawba would have
difficulty in placing him. But historians will remember
him as a leader in the affairs of his own state for almost
fifty years; as an able and resourceful Governor; later, as
one of the more forceful and colorful leaders of debate
in the affairs of the United States Senate; and all in all,
when the whole record of his life is weighed and estimated, as a man of great natural ability and intelligence, considering his place and time and situation.

He directed the affairs of his state through the Civil
War, and he directed them courageously and ably. In
periods of stress he was unmoved by threat and un-
swayed by the hysterias of popular feeling. In the closing
days of the Confederacy, when the armies were in desperate need, he curtly refused a demand from Jefferson
Davis for almost seventy thousand suits of uniforms,
shoes, and coats which the state owned and had in its
possession. He refused bluntly and without apology,

saying that the equipment would be used first of all for the rehabilitation of his own people; and although this act of rebellion brought down upon him bitter denunciation from all quarters, he stuck to his decision and refused to budge.

Later, in the darker days of Reconstruction, military occupation, black legislatures, and night riders, he rendered even greater service to his state. And he concluded a long life, full of honors and accomplishment, as a member of the nation's Senate, in which capacity he died, during Cleveland's last administration, in 1893.

All these facts are sufficiently well known to make his position in the nation's chronicle secure. But to people in Catawba his name means a great deal more than this. They are well acquainted with the story of his life, and the record of his offices as it has been outlined here. But these honors and accomplishments, splendid as they are, do not in themselves explain the place he holds in Catawba's heart. For he is their hero: in the most local and particular sense, they feel that he belongs to them, is of them, could in no conceivable way belong to anything else, is theirs and theirs alone. Therefore, they love him.

He was not only their own native Lincoln—their backwoods son who marched to glory by the log-rail route—he was their Crockett and Paul Bunyan rolled in one. He was not alone their hero; he was their legend and their myth. He was, and has remained so to this day, a kind of living prophecy of all that they themselves might wish to be; a native divinity, shaped out of their own clay, and breathing their own air; a tongue that spoke the words, a voice that understood and spoke the language, they would have him speak.

They tell a thousand stories about him today. What does it matter if many of the things which they describe never happened? They are true because they are the kind of things he would have said, the kind of things that would have happened to him. Thus, to what degree, and in what complex ways, he was created so in their imaginations, no one can say. How much the man shaped the myth, how much the myth shaped the man, how much Zack Joyner created his own folk, or how much his people created him—no one can know, and it does not matter.

For he was of them, and the rib; and they of him the body and the flesh. He was indigenous to them as their own clay, as much a part of all their lives as the geography of their native earth, the climate of their special weather. No other place on earth but Old Catawba could have produced him. And the people know this: therefore, again, they love him.

In examining the history of that great man, we have collected more than eight hundred stories, anecdotes, and jokes that are told of him, and of this number at least six hundred have the unmistakable ring—or *smack* —of truth. If they did not happen—they *should* have! They belong to him: they fit him like an old shoe.

"But," the pedants cunningly inquire, "*did* they happen? Now, really, *did* they? Ah, yes, they *sound* like him—he *might* have said them—but that's not the point! *Did* he?"

Well, we are not wholly unprepared for these objections. Of the six hundred stories which have the smack of truth, we have actually verified three hundred as authentic beyond the shadow of a doubt, and are ready to cite them by the book—place, time, occasion, evidence—to anyone who may inquire. In these stories there is a strength, a humor, a coarseness, and a native originality that belonged to the man and marked his every utterance. They come straight out of his own earth.

As a result of our researches, we can state unequivocally that there is no foundation in fact for the story that one time, in answer to a lady's wish, he called out to a Negro urchin at a station curb, who had a donkey wagon and a load of peanuts:

"Boy! Back your —— over here and show this lady your ——!"

But he certainly did make the speech in the United States Senate (in rejoinder to the Honorable Barnaby Bulwinkle) that is generally accredited to him, even though there is no account of it in the *Congressional Record*:

"Mr. President, sir, we are asked by the honorable gentleman to appropriate two hundred thousand dollars of the taxpayers' money for the purpose of building a bridge across Coon Creek in the honorable gentleman's district—a stream, sir, which I have seen, and which, sir, I assure you, I could —— halfway across."

The Vice-President (pounding with his gavel): "The Senator is out of order."

Senator Joyner: "Mr. President, sir, you are right. If I was *in* order, sir, I could —— the whole way across it!"

The last story that is told of Zachariah Joyner is that in his final days of illness (and, like King Charles, in dying, he was "an unconscionable time") he was aroused from coma one afternoon by the sound of rapid hoofs and wheels, and, looking wearily out of the window of his room, he saw the spare figure of his brother Rufus hastening toward the house. Even in his last extremity his humor did not forsake him, for he is said to have smiled wanly and feebly croaked:

"My God! I reckon it's all up with me! For here comes Rufe!"

People told the story later and, despite the grimness of the joke, they laughed at it; for the family trait to which it pointed was well known.

Bear Joyner, in his later years, after he had moved to Libya Hill, when told of the death of one of his sons in Zebulon by his second marriage, is known to have said:

"Well, I reckon some of the children will attend the funeral." Here he considered seriously a moment, then nodded his head with an air of confirmation. "Hit's— hit's no more than right!" And after another pause he added virtuously: "If I was thar, *I'd go myself!*" And with these words, he wagged his head quite solemnly, in such a way as to leave no doubt about the seriousness of his intent.

Zachariah is reported, when asked the number of his kin, to have replied: "Hell, I don't know! You can't throw a rock in Zebulon without hitting one of them!" He reflected on his metaphor a moment, and then said: "However, let him that is without sin among you throw the first stone. I can't!" And with these words he turned virtuously away, scratching himself vigorously in the behind.

Again, when he responded to the greeting of a member of the audience after a political rally at which he had made a speech, he is reported to have said:

"My friend, your face looks familiar to me. Haven't I seen you somewhere before?"

To which the person so addressed replied: "Yes, sir. I think you have. I was yore pappy's ninth child by his second marriage, and you was his fourth 'un by his first. So I reckon you might say that you and me was both half-brothers, distantly removed."

The grimmest story in the whole Joyner catalogue, perhaps, is that old Bear Joyner, when reproached one time for a seeming neglect of his own brood, is reputed to have said to his inquisitor:

"My God Almighty! A man can plant the seed, but he cain't make the weather! I sowed 'em—now, goddamn 'em, let 'em grow!"

There is no reason to believe that either William or his children were as neglectful of each other as these stories indicate, yet they really do denote a trait—or failing—of the clan. The fault—if fault it be—has long been known in Catawba, where it is said that "the only thing that will bring 'em all together is a wedding or a funeral; and it has to be a good one to do that." And yet, this trait has been too easily interpreted. Many people have taken such stories as evidence that the Joyners were lacking in a sense of family feeling; but nothing could be further from the truth.

The truth is that no family ever lived that had a stronger sense of their identity. It is hard to describe the thing in more familiar terms, for the whole tribe violates the standards by which such things are com-

monly appraised. Of "affection," "love," "devotion,"
even "clannishness"—as these terms are generally accepted—the family seems to have had little. It is perfectly true that years have gone by when brothers have
not seen or spoken to each other, even when they lived
in the same town. It is also true that some have grown
rich, indifferent to others who have struggled on in
obscure poverty; that children have been born, and
grown up, and gone away, scarcely familiar with the
look of a cousin's face, the identity of a cousin's name.

Many people have observed these things and wondered at them, and then accepted them as further proof
that the tribe was "queer." And yet, paradoxically, out
of this very indifference came the family unity. From
this very separateness came the deep and lasting sense
of their identity. In a way, they reversed completely the
old adage that if men refuse to hang together, they will
all hang separately: of the Joyners it could rather be
said that they hang separately because they know they
hang together.

To find what produced their sense of "separateness"
one must look into the history of the family.

The many children of Bear Joyner by his two mar-
riages—there were more than twenty by the lowest
count—grew up in a community where every man had
to look out for himself. As for old Bill himself, nothing
in his earlier life had prepared him for the exacting
duties of parenthood. Whatever his career had been
before he came into the hill-bound fastnesses of Zebulon,
it had been very hard. He is known to have said: "If a
young'un don't learn to root afore fourteen, he never
will. A hen'll scrabble for young chicks, but before
they're fryin' size they've got to scratch for themselves."

Although he was a man of substance for his time and
place, his means were not enough to give two dozen
children an easy start in life. Moreover, it must be
owned that, like so many men who have been widowed
in first marriage, he ventured into a second because it
was the best expedient to meet his need. And the four-

teen or sixteen children who came later—well, it is a brutal fact, but it was a sowing of blind seed. They came. They just came. And that was all.

Perhaps it is unjust to emphasize the schism of this second marriage. And yet, a separation did exist. It is inevitable that this should have been. For one thing, the older children of Bear Joyner's first marriage were fairly well grown when he married for the second time, and when the children of the second brood began to come along. Again, the surviving children of the first— Zack, Robert, Hattie, Theodore, and Rufe—were, if not a different breed, yet of a separate clan. And they knew it. From the first, instinctively, they seemed to know it. It was not that, consciously, they felt themselves to be "superior"—a bitter accusation that was later made—and yet they seemed to feel they were. And—since the blunt truth must be spoken—in the light of their accomplishment, and in the world's esteem, they were.

Another fact—the Joyners, first to last, were a vainglorious folk. Even old William had his share of this defect, perhaps even more than the rest of them, for old men thirty years ago who could remember him, and who would pay due tribute to his prowess and his extraordinary gifts, would often add: "Well, he *knowed* that he was good. . . . He was remarkable, but he *knowed* that he was good. And he was bigoted. He could be bigoted; and he was overbearing, too. . . . And as for Zack," old men would smile when they said his name, "Well, there was Zack, too. He knowed that *he* was good. Zack was a wonder . . . but no one ever said he was a blushing violet."

The Joyners of this early flowering not only "knowed that they was good," but they made little effort to conceal it. Apparently, none of them—unless it was Robert—hid his light under a bushel. And the truth is, each of them, in his own way—even Theodore!—had a light to show.

The reasons? Well, the reasons were complex, but perhaps the first one was the consciousness they had of special heritage. Bear Joyner's first wife was a "special woman": she was a Creasman, and the Creasmans were "good people." The Joyners of the first lot were all proud of their Creasman ancestry. Of Martha Creasman herself there is little to be told except that she was a good wife, a quiet and hard-working mother, and a Presbyterian. This last fact, trifling as it seems, was all important: for it bespeaks a kind of denominational snobbishness which is still more prevalent than the world may know, and which the Joyners of the first lot never lost.

As to Bear Joyner's second wife, she was a Baptist. The first Joyners—Zack, and all the rest of them—were always careful to speak of her respectfully, but with a touch of unconscious patronage that was infuriating to "the country cousins" of the lesser breed:

"Well now, she was a mighty good woman, and all of that. . . . Of course"—with a kind of hesitant and regretful concessiveness—"she was a Baptist. . . . I reckon you might call her a kind of religious fanatic. . . . She had queer religious notions. . . . But she was a good woman. . . . She had some queer ideas, but she was a good mother to those children. . . . Now everyone will have to give her *that!*"

Here then, obviously, were the roots of the great schism. Bear Joyner himself seems to have shared unconsciously in this prejudice of his elder children. He had apparently always been somewhat in awe of his first wife: her family was well known, and there is reason to believe he felt he was making a considerable step forward in the world when he married her. Toward his second wife he had no such feeling: she was one of a hard-shell Baptist tribe, and there is a story that he met her at camp meeting. However that may be, he was "looking for a woman to keep house"; and it was pretty much in this capacity that he married her.

That she worked long and faithfully there can be no doubt; or that she was a patient, strong, enduring woman—"a good mother," as the elder Joyners always

willingly admitted, to the numerous family that she
now began to bring into the world.

As for Bear Joyner's older children by his previous
marriage—Zack, Hattie, Robert, Theodore, and Rufe
(Martha and George, the two remaining of the seven,
had died in childhood)—they seem from the beginning
to have been outside the sphere of their stepmother's
control. Their strongly marked individualities had already been defined and shaped by the time their father
married again. They had inherited, in liberal measure,
his own strong character, his arrogant confidence in his
own powers, a good measure of his color, his independence, his intelligence, his coarse and swinging humor, his quick wit.

There is no evidence that they were consciously
contemptuous of their new mother, but there is no
doubt they felt superior to her. Even in a backwoods
community theirs was a larger, bolder, more tolerant
and experienced view of life than she had ever known;
and her narrow prejudice, her cramped vision, her rigid
small moralities (all products of an inheritance she
couldn't help) simply amused them, aroused their ridicule and mirth.

Zachariah, especially, although in later years he always spoke feelingly of her excellent qualities, was particularly active in his humorous analysis of her. Her
superstitions and prejudices amused him; the operations
of her mind, and the narrow cells of her morality
seemed grotesque and ludicrous to him; and he questioned, teased, examined her rather cruelly in order, as
he said, "to see what made her tick."

Hers, indeed, poor woman, was a strange and contra-
dictory code, and yet, because it was the only one she
knew, she thought it was the only one there was: it
seemed natural to her, and it never occurred to her to
question it.

That harsh code to which she adhered was indigenous to America. It has not only done much to shape
our lives and histories, but it persists to this day, and is

at the root of much of the sickness, the moral complex
of America. For example, she believed it was wrong to
take a life "in cold blood," but it was not nearly so
wrong as to take a drink. She was always warning her
children against evil ways and loose living, and speaking
of people who committed "all kinds of immorality and
licentiousness"; but it would have come strangely to her
ears to hear murder referred to as an immoral act. True,
it was "an awful crime"—she could understand it in
these terms because the Bible told about Cain and
Abel, and taught that it was wicked to take life. But,
privately, she did not consider it half as bad for a man
to take a life as to take a drink, or—what was the most
immoral act of all—to sleep with a woman who was
not his wife.

Life-taking, the shedding of man's blood, was so
much a part of the life of a pioneer community that it
occasioned no surprise. To be sure, she would not
openly defend the practice of killing, although in a
surprising number of individual cases she was willing to
defend it, becoming quite aroused, in fact, when Zachariah, with deceptive gravity, would point out that
her own brother—whose life in other ways she esteemed as a model of the Christian virtues—had been
quite handy with his gun in his hot youth, and was
known to have killed three men:

"Now, Zack," she would cry angrily, "don't you go
a-diggin' into that. Reese had his faults, like everyone,
and I reckon maybe in his young days he may have
been hot-tempered. But he's always led a good Christian and God-fearin' sort of life. He never drank or
smoked or used bad language or ran around with
women—like *some* people I know about." Here she
glared accusingly at her erring stepson, who returned
her look with an expression of bland innocence. "So
don't you start on him: he's always been an upright,
moral sort of man."

All of this amused Zachariah no end: he did not
mean to be cruel to her, but, as she said, he was "always tormenting" her, rummaging gravely about in the

confusing rag-bag of her moral consciousness to see what further mysteries would be revealed.

He is known to have spoken of the physical sharpness of her sense of smell, which really was amazing, and which all of her children inherited (she is said one time to have "smelled burning leaves five miles away upon the mountain, long before anyone else knowed there was a fire"):

"Well, she can smell fire and brimstone farther off than that. And Hell! If I took a drink in Libya Hill, she'd smell it on my breath before I crossed the county line!"

On another occasion, she is said to have called out to him the moment that he came into the house: "Zack Joyner! You've been drinkin' that bad, old, rotten, vile corn licker again. I can smell it on your breath!"

"Now, mother," he answered temperately, "there is no bad, old, rotten, vile corn licker. Some is good—" he went on in a tone of judicious appraisal that she must have found very hard to take—"and some is better. But there is no bad!"

Again, when Bear Joyner returned from Libya Hill one day with this announcement:

"Well, Thad Burton's gone and done it again!"

"Gone and done what?" said Zachariah, looking up.

"Gone and killed a man," Bear Joyner answered.

"Oh!" said Zachariah with a relieved air, casting a sly look toward his stepmother, "I was afraid you were goin' to tell me he'd done something really bad, like gettin' drunk."

Bear Joyner was no less adept than his sons in this sport of teasing his bewildered wife. It is said that having driven in with her one day from Zebulon, to see the boys who at that time were "keeping store" for him in Libya Hill, he went into the store and, finding Zack on duty there, the following conversation then took place between them:

"You boys been leadin' the Christ-life like your mother told you to?"

"Yes, sir," Zachariah said.

"Have you done your chores this mornin'?"

"Yes, sir."

"Watered the milk?"

"Yes, sir."

"Sanded the sugar?"

"Yes, sir."

"*Fixed* the scales?"

"Yes, sir."

"Well," said Bear, "you'd better call in Ted and Bob. Your mother's here, an' we're goin' to have prayers."

Finally, there was the case of Harriet—the "Miss Hattie" of later years, for she never married—to add to the confusion and distress of William Joyner's second wife. Of all Bear Joyner's children, Hattie was the favorite. In her, perhaps, more than in any of the others he saw the qualities—the quick wit, the humor, the independence and intelligence—that in himself he most esteemed. It has been said she was his "love child"—a euphemism maybe for the fact that she was illegitimate —and that this accounted for her father's deeper care. At any rate, although her birth was hidden in an obscurity that was never cleared—for old Bear Joyner never spoke of it, and no one dared to speak of it to him— she was brought up as a member of his elder brood. The story goes that he was gone one time for several weeks upon a journey to the south, and that when he returned he brought the child with him. She was almost eight years old then, and Martha, the first wife, was still alive. The story goes that Joyner brought the child into the house—the family was at dinner, and the faces of the other children wonderingly turned—and sat her down beside them at the table.

"This," he said, "is your new sister. From this time on, she'll be one of the family, and you'll treat her so."

And this is all that was ever spoken. It is said that Martha, Joyner's first wife, took the child as one of her own; and in justice to the second wife, no matter what additional distress and confusion this new proof of Joyner wickedness may have caused that bewildered woman's soul, it was always freely acknowledged, most loyally of all by Harriet herself, as a further tribute to the woman's qualities, that she was a good mother, and brought the girl up as if she were "one of her own."

Historically, time-periods are most curiously defined: the world does not grow up together. The footpads that made Johnson carry his stick at night when he went out alone in London in the Eighteenth Century have been quite actively abroad in recent years in our own land. And as for "human life," a commodity which our editorial writers tell us they most jealously esteem, the security of human life in our own broad land—whether from murder, violence, or sudden death of every kind soever—is perhaps *almost* as great in America at the present time as it was in England at the period of Elizabeth, although our figures are by far the more bloody of the two.

And as for our own Dick Whittingtons—our country boys who went to town—there, too, we ape the European pattern; but we have been late.

The history of human celebrity for the most part is an urban one. In our own land, although children are taught that most of their great men "came from the country," it is not sufficiently emphasized that most of them also "went to town." Certainly, this has been true in America: the national history could almost be written in the lives of men who went to town.

Zachariah Joyner, in his later years, was very fond of using the log-cabin theme for politics, but if he had been more true to fact, he would have admitted that the turning point in his own career had come when he abandoned finally the world-lost fastnesses of Zebulon for the more urban settlement of Libya Hill. There, truly, was *his* starting point, his threshold, the step from which he gained his vantage, took off for the larger community of public life and general notice in which for fifty years he was to play so large a role.

And, in various ways, the same transitional experience was true of his more immediate family—his three brothers, who came with him. In one sense the whole history of the many Joyners, their divided lot and the boundary that separated the lowly from the great, might be stated in one phrase. It was the history of those who stayed at home, and of those who went to town.

As the years passed, the division of each group became more widely marked, the sense of unity more faint and far. Hillbound, world-lost, locked in the narrow valleys and the mountain walls of Zebulon, the Joyners who remained at home became almost as strange and far away to those who lived in Libya Hill as if their home had been the Mountains of the Moon. True, they lived only fifty miles away, but as Bear Joyner had himself said so many years before, it was "the wrong way." It really was this sense of two directions that divided them. The Libya Hill Joyners were facing ever toward the world, and those in Zebulon away from it; and as years went by, it seemed that this directiveness became more marked than ever—the town Joyners ever more the world's men; those in Zebulon more withdrawn from the world.

By 1900, a whole century since William Joyner crossed the Blue Ridge and came down into the wilderness with his rifle and his grant of land, if some curious historian, gifted with immortality, could have returned there, he would have observed a change as startling as it was profound. He would have found the lives of the town Joyners (for by this time Libya Hill had grown to twelve thousand people) so greatly altered as to be scarcely recognizable; but he would have found the lives of the country Joyners scarcely changed at all.

True, some changes had occurred in Zebulon in those hundred years, but for the most part these were tragic ones. The great mountain slopes and forests of the section had been ruinously detimbered; the farm-soil on hill sides had eroded and washed down; high up, upon the hills, one saw the raw scars of old mica pits, the dump heaps of deserted mines. Some vast destructive "Suck" had been at work here; and a visitor, had he returned after one hundred years, would have been compelled to note the ruin of the change. It was evident that a huge compulsive greed had been at work: the whole region had been sucked and gutted, milked dry, denuded of its rich primeval treasures: something blind and ruthless had been here, grasped, and gone. The blind scars on the hills, the denuded slopes, the empty mica pits were what was left.

And true, the hills were left—with these deteriorations; and all around, far-flung in their great barricades, the immense wild grandeur of the mountain wall, the great Blue Ridge across which they had come long, long ago; and which had held them from the world.

And the old formations of the earth were left: the boiling clamor of the rocky streams, the cool slant darkness of the mountain hollows. Something wild, world-lost, and lyrical, and special to the place called Zebulon was somehow left: the sound of rock-bright waters, bird calls, and something swift and fleeting in a wood; the way light comes and goes; cloud shadows passing on a hill; the wind through the hill grasses, and the quality of light—something world-lost, far, and haunting (special to the place as is the very climate of the soil) in the quality of light; and little shacks and cabins stuck to hill or hollow, sunken, tiny, in the gap; the small, heart-piercing wisps of smoke that coiled into the clear immensity of weather from some mountain shack, with its poignant evidence that men fasten to a ledge, and draw their living from a patch of earth—because they have been here so long and love it and cannot be made to leave; together with lost voices of one's kinsmen long ago—all this was left, but their inheritance was bare. Something had come into the wilderness, and had left the barren land.

And the people—ah, the people!—yes, the people——

They were left! They were left "singing the same songs" (as college Doctors of Philosophy so gloatingly

assure us) "their Elizabethan forebears sang"—which is
a falsehood; and no glory—they should have made new
and better ones for themselves. "Speaking the same
tongue" their Elizabethan forebears spoke—which also
is a falsehood; and they should have made a new one
for themselves. "Living the same lives" their forebears
lived a hundred years ago—which further is a
falsehood. The lives their forebears lived were harsh
and new, still seeking and explorative; their own lives
often were just squalid, which should have been better.

What remained? It has been said, "The earth remains." But this was wrong. The earth had changed,
the earth had eroded, the earth had washed down the
gulleys in a billion runnels of red clay; the earth was
gone.

But the people—ah, the people!—yes, the people!
The people were still there!

Turned backwards now, world-lost, in what was once
new land! Unseeking now, in what their forebears with
blue vistas in their eyes, alone, in Indian country,
sought! Turned in upon themselves, congruent as a
tribe, all intermarried (so each man now was cousin to
the very blood he took: each Cain among them brother
to his very deed!)——

The people!—aye, the people! The people of Zack
Joyner, and old Bear, who sought a world, and *found* it,
that such as these might lose it; had wandered so that
such as these should *stay*; had sought great vistas to the
West, so that such as these remain——

The people! To be gloated over by exultant Ph.D.'s
(who find in mountain shacks the accents of
Elizabeth); to be gawked at by tourists (now the roads
are good) in search of the rare picturesque; to be
yearned over by consecrated school-marms "from the
North"; have their "standards" "improved" by social
service workers, who dote upon the squalor, ignorance,
and poverty; lasciviously regret the degradations of the
people's lot, and who do valiantly their little bit (God
bless their little, little souls!) to help the people, teach
the people, prop the people, *heal* the people, with their

little salves (not too completely, else what are little salves and social service work about?)—and who therefore (in spite of dirt, filth, rickets, murder, lean-tos, children, syphilis, hunger, incest, and pellagra) love the people, adore the people, see underneath their "drawbacks" and their "lack of opportunities" all "the good" in people—because the people, at the bottom, "are so fine."

It is a lie! . . . Dear God! . . . Dear Jesus God, protect us, all men living, and the people, from such stuff as this!

The people are not "fine"—the people are not picturesque—the people——

Well, after a hundred years of it—denudings, minings, lootings, intermarryings, killings, dyings, bornings, livings, all the rest of it—the people—in spite of Smike, the lumber thief, who stole their hills; and Snead, his son, who stole their balladry; in spite of Gripe, who took their mica and their ore, and gave them "the lung-sickness" in exchange for it; despite Grace, Gripe's daughter, who now brings rubber condoms and tuberculin; and his wife, Gertrude, who schools them in hand-weaving—despite Gripe, Smike, and Grace, and all lovers of the picturesque soever—despite rickets, incest, syphilis, and sham—the people! —ah, the people!—well, the *people*——

"Why, goddamn it!" Zachariah Joyner roared— "I'll tell you what the people are! . . . The people . . . the *people!* . . . Why, goddamn it, sir, the people are the *people!*"

And so they are!—Smike, Gripe, rickets, Grace, and Snead—all forces to the contrary notwithstanding.

The people are the people.

And the Joyners—second Joyners; the humble, world-lost Joyners out in Zebulon—they're the people!

CHAPTER IV

How Certain Joyners Went to Town

Bear Joyner was what would be called today "a forward-looking man." He had not been settled down in Zebulon very long before he began to regret the choice that had brought him there, saying: "Hit's too *fer back!* Hit's purty, but you can't git *out!*"

Here was the spirit of the empire-builder. He was not, in his own phrase, a man to "crawl into a hole and pull it in after him." If there was an "in," there must also be an "out"—and soon after he came to Zebulon he began to look for it.

During the next twenty years his life was punctuated by his explorations, which, comparatively short though they were, were most significant. Throughout those two decades, restless, seeking, forever unsatisfied, he was still "looking for the place." In this period of his early manhood he seems to have been regarded with misgivings by his neighbors in Zebulon, especially by the older and more conservative element. His good qualities—his energy, his skill, his strength, and his intelligence—were recognized and esteemed, but there was a strong suspicion that he was by temperament a rolling stone, and that his worldly fortunes would never flourish because he would not stay at home long enough to allow them to take root.

At first, his life was that of the woodsman and trapper. He fished, he hunted, and he had his little patch of land where he could grow such food as he needed.

Wild game, including bear and venison, was plentiful. Even after his first marriage, this is the way he continued to live, in the cabin on the south fork of the Toe.

But in those early years, as people told it later, he was forever "up and gone." He would go off on long hunting trips, or on mysterious expeditions into the surrounding country. Sometimes these journeys took him into Tennessee, or down to South Carolina, or eastward across the Blue Ridge to the Piedmont, or even far north into Virginia. He would be gone for days, sometimes for weeks, "leavin' that woman out thar all alone." There were forebodings and grave shakings of the head; but while the others stayed at home, Bear Joyner saw new lands.

People admitted freely that he "knew more about this country" than any other person living there. And his restless explorations were to bear fruit in unsuspected ways. Gradually he acquired a kind of gigantic mental blueprint of the whole region for a hundred miles around, until there was scarcely a stream, a creek, a valley, or a hollow in that vast wilderness which he did not know. Little by little, his knowledge began to define itself more clearly and to shape his moves, until at last it led him to Libya Hill.

Libya Hill is a sort of great encampment in the hills, the tenting ground of the Blue Ridge. It is on a high plateau, close-held against the east, and again in semicircles to the north and south, by a border of low hills, but opening to the west, and the soaring vistas of the western ranges forty miles away. The great ranges come down to the rolling slopes of Libya Hill like lions to a water-hole; and westward, northward, southward, eastward, in smoky vistas the great ranges soar away. When Bear Joyner first saw it he said, as Brigham Young was to say a little later of another spot: "This is the place."

It was, indeed, of all that mountain district of the west, "the place." It was a natural confluence of the hills, the junction of the four directions of the map— the appointed, the inevitable, place. A river, broader than any of the small streams of Zebulon, wound through the passes of the hills into the West. Along the narrow valley of another winding stream another road was open to the East. Here was the place, not only where the world got out, but also where the world got in.

Bear Joyner saw this; and here at last, for him, was journey's end. From this time on, the story of his life is the story of his withdrawings out of Zebulon toward this chosen place. In the end he took the four sons of his first marriage with him; and he left the rest behind. The Joyners at last had come to town. Thence dates the final schism of the clan, as well as the beginning of its greater history.

By 1828 Bear Joyner owned the country store in Libya Hill—the largest one in the whole section—and thenceforth his fortunes were secure. In the years that followed, before the end of his long life, he bought up various tracts of land, and these were ultimately dispersed among the "four town Joyners" who became his heirs.

Indeed, as recently as sixty years ago, when Libya Hill had grown to perhaps two thousand people, the Joyner heirs still held large tracts of land. And even in this present century children were familiar with the regretful recollections of their elders, who could recall when "Rufus Joyner offered me that whole block— from where the Palais Royal now stands all the way down to the Post Office corner—for *two hundred dollars!* And I was such a fool I didn't take it! If I had, I'd have been a rich man today. You couldn't buy it now for a million dollars! But then—why, I just laughed at him. It was nothing but an old field, with a pig pen in the hollow, and the hogs used to wallow in the mud where Main Street is today. Two hundred dollars for that hole? I thought Rufe Joyner must be crazy; or else he took me for a fool. 'All right,' he said. 'You wait and see.' Well, I waited, and I did!"

By the time the Civil War broke out the Joyners were accounted wealthy folk. It was "the big family" of the whole community. Even long before that their position was so generally acknowledged throughout the western mountains that when the boys began to "make their mark," it occasioned no surprise.

When Zack Joyner was Governor of the state, and later United States Senator, he was fond of saying, for purposes political, that he had been "raised on hawg and hominy."

"I have known what it was," he would say, warming up to his subject, and dropping into the mountain idiom for the benefit of his delighted followers—"I've known what it was, boys, to go to bed on bacon and awake on grits. Yes, and I've known what it was to go to bed and to git up without either of 'em. I have clumb the persimmon tree many's the time to shrink my belly up to fit my rations, so don't talk to me of no hard times. I can go right out into the cornfield or the tobacco patch and spit on my hands and keep up with any man that's settin' here tonight. If I was twenty years younger, I'd give ye all a head start and beat ye."

Like so many other specimens of political autobiography, this was a good deal less than accurate. Far from being the barefoot and half-starved infant born in a humble cabin—the image which he was fondest of evoking—Zack had been brought up under circumstances which were amazingly comfortable for the time and place. Before he was half grown, his father was already considered well off and was one of the leading citizens of the town. Zack's public statements about himself were simply part of the legend which he created, and which helped to create him—the legend of the backwoods savior, the country Moses, schooled by poverty, hardship, solitude, and the precepts of a stern and homely virtue, until at last he had been ready to come out of the wilderness and lead his people into the promised land.

In elaboration of the log-cabin theme, Zack would say that "all the schoolin' I ever had would not amount to three months put together, and even then I had to walk six miles for what I got." This, too, was part of the myth on which great Zachariah's life was founded. Privately, he would confess that he knew how to "read and write and cipher" before he came to Libya Hill. And there is proof that he, along with Theodore and Robert, attended school in Libya Hill for some time under the tutelage of a pedagogue who was always referred to later by the Joyners with considerable respect as "Old Professor Coleman." Zack managed to learn, among other things, a smattering of Latin, for even in his old age he could quote from *Caesar's Gallic Wars*.

In talking with his closer friends, he would admit something of the truth and say good-naturedly: "Well, it wasn't a great deal, but it was something. Bob, Ted, and I learned how to read and write and cipher. And *Uriah!*"—this was his familiar name for Rufus when his older brother was not present (an indication that he knew his Dickens, too)—"Uriah," chuckled Zack, "he never took the time to read or write, but, by God!"— here his shoulders would begin to heave—"*Uriah* always did know how to cipher!"

Rufus, the oldest of the four, was, by general consent and his own choice, the storekeeper of the crowd. Of his career, all that need be set forth here are the bare facts. And the bare facts in Rufe's case are peculiarly appropriate, for his was a bare life, a grooved life, a hard-bitten, steady, quiet life which from first to last, with one exception, was to run on a single track. The first great exception, of course, was the Civil War. When the call came he went to war, he lived through the war, he came back from the war, and that was the only interruption that his purpose suffered. And his purpose was business. His purpose was money. That was all he ever did or thought about. He never married. He carried on his father's business, he built it into a really great enterprise, and he became a rich man. Of any man, perhaps all that can be truly said when his life is done is that "he lived, he suffered, and he died." With the same succinct finality it would later be said of Rufus: "He made money, and he died."

Meanwhile he lived in his father's old house on College Street. Eventually his lusty, gusty, old-maid sister, Hattie, came from Zebulon to keep house for him. But not all the wit and savor, the irrepressible spirits and joy of living that animated the sprightly figure of Miss Hattie Joyner could ever deflect Rufus from his grim purpose. Even in his youth his stinginess was proverbial, and in his old age his brother, Zachariah, then also hale and sere, had no hesitation in proclaiming it:

"Why, he's so mean," Zack roared, "he wouldn't —— down a preacher's throat if his guts were on fire! If you fell down and broke your leg he wouldn't come across the street to help you because of the shoe leather he'd use up. He stops the clocks at night to keep the cogs from wearing out, and when he goes to church he puts a two-cent stamp in the collection plate and takes back a penny's change!"

Hattie, who was more like Zachariah in her ribald humor than any of the others, and who outlived all of them, would cackle gleefully and say: "Just wait till that old skinflint dies! I'll beat him yet—even if I have to live to be a hundred. When he's gone I'm goin' to open up the purse strings and let the moths fly out! I tell you, I'm just waitin' till he dies *to cut loose and raise hell!*"

In the course of this chronicle we have mentioned the fact that old Bear Joyner had some fourteen or sixteen children by his second wife, all of whom were left behind in Zebulon when their father came to Libya Hill. He did not exactly leave them, for he was always going back for visits—the point is that he did not bring them with him, and they did not have gumption enough to insist on coming. We have not yet had occasion to tell about these members of the lesser breed, although they all had Christian names like other folk. Of those who survived the rigors of infancy and childhood there were, among the girls, Betsy, Alice, Melissa, and Florabelle, and, among the boys, Lafayette, Sam, John, Claudius, Sid, and Rance. Insofar as they get into our story, each of these shall have his due in time. For the present they will have to look after themselves. We have left them behind in the fastnesses of Zebulon County where they made their bed, and there they will have to lie in it. They would not come along with us. They did not have it in them to push on with the Joyners of the great will, the great spirit, the great determination. Therefore we shall now leave them to the honorable but mute oblivion of unrecorded history, and shall forget about them until the turn of events compels us to seek them out again.

Suffice it to say that they grew up and married and had children and grandchildren. They tilled the soil, they grew much corn and tobacco, they timbered the rugged slopes of Zebulon for Smike, the lumber thief, and mined for feldspar and for mica in the wretched pay of Gripe, Smike's brother, until the very wilderness which had been their sole inheritance became scarred and barren. They despoiled the land, and were in turn themselves despoiled. But still they were very worthy and honest people. There were few horse thieves among them, and only two or three of them got hanged. Just the same, it must be owned that they were small potatoes. They did not join the Joyners of the greater breed. They never went to town—none of them, that is, except for Lafayette, and he came late, and the reasons for his coming were of quite another order from those which had moved his half-brothers years before. But of that, more anon. To everything its season, and our story now concerns the Joyners of the first coming.

To be sure, it was not very much of a town that these first Joyners came to—unless "a hole in the road," a log courthouse of one room, a log church, a general store, a hitching post, and a ramshackle tavern for itinerant drovers could be called a town. But the fact remains that town it was—town in the core, in the making, in the process of becoming. Libya Hill was at that time the only semblance of a town that the whole mountain district could boast of.

When Bear Joyner became the owner of the general

store and his fortunes began to flourish, he gave to his four favorite sons the education that each was fitted for. While Rufus settled down to keeping store like one who had been born for it, Zachariah, Robert, and Theodore were sent away, in turn, to college.

At just what time in Zachariah's formative years the idea of the law as a career first came to him, it is impossible to say; but it came early, and the choice was inevitable. As a boy of eighteen, when he was helping Rufe to "tend store" for their father, he was already noted for his ready wit, his coarse humor, and his gift of repartee. People would come into the store "just to hear Zack Joyner talk."

And even in that backwoods community there was a pretty shrewd appraisal of him from the first. Already people suspected, or observed, more than a trace of charlatanism in his make-up. It was said: "He can talk you *out* or talk you *in* to anything." Among other tendencies that many noticed in him was a certain indisposition to hard work. Bear Joyner himself was well aware of this, because he said: "Well, I don't know what to do with him unless I make a lawyer of him. He won't *work*—that's certain." Here he paused a moment; then he grinned and added: "But he won't starve, neither. Not Zack."

It may be that there is wisdom in the observation of the showman that "the people like to be fooled." Anyhow, the experience of Zack Joyner's life would seem to bear this out. For the very basis of his amazing political success lay in the people's *awareness* of him: not only the fact that they knew him so well, but also that he was so much *of* them, as if they felt him to be, in some special way, their own. And among the qualities which people seemed most to admire in Zack, and to be proud of rather than otherwise, was his tincture of charlatanism and smooth dealing. They loved to tell stories to illustrate Zack's smartness, his adeptness, his superior adroitness and cunning, and men would wag their heads and laugh with envious approval, as though they wished they could do such things themselves, but knew, being merely average men, that they could not make the grade.

So Zack was sent away for a year of legal training at Pine Rock College (a year was considered ample in those days). Bob followed him there and also had his year of training for the law. Then both boys returned home again, were admitted to the bar, and hung out their shingle as the firm of Joyner and Joyner. By 1840 they were enjoying a thriving practice. For in that day the fact that the two Joyner boys had become full-fledged lawyers—this very same Zack and Bob whom everybody in town had known and liked and watched grow up—was quite a thing to marvel at and feel a sense of personal pride in.

Lawyers, of course—that articulate tribe which was to breed and multiply with such astonishing proliferation during the next century—were not utterly foreign to the little town. From its beginnings Libya Hill had been the county seat, and had had its courthouse, its circuit judges, and its trials for thirty years or more. But the Joyners were the first lawyers to come of local stock. The others heretofore had been imported.

These other lawyers had come in to the sessions of the court from older and more populous communities beyond the Blue Ridge—from Old Stockade, from Millerton, from Locust Gap—and occasionally from still larger towns farther east, down in the Piedmont. They had come in by stage, by coach, by horse and saddle. They had come in with their frocktails parted across the cruppers of their horses, with long and spindly legs hung loosely down around the shining flanks. They had come in with their jaws lank and learned, their thin lips closed, their cold eyes ruminant and speculative, narrowed into slits, their saddlebags stuffed with all the cunning of their accursed and incessant papers. They had come in and dismounted and tied up at the hitching post before the log courthouse, had swung their bony hands beneath their coattails and carried in the saddlebags and unpacked their papers, and then had

spoken strange words—strange words of depth and learning no one else could understand. While all the help-
less natives looked on and gaped their wonderment, the
great men cleared their throats and uttered strange and
mystic words and shuffled their accursed papers in their
parchment fingers. And, so speaking and so doing, they
had then departed, leaving native awe behind them,
taking with them native fees.

Now this was changed. The Joyner boys had gone
away beyond the Blue Ridge, farther off than anyone
else had ever been, had seen strange peoples and
strange cities, and had got much learning—deep learning, lawyer learning—and now could speak and write
the mystic words that no one else could read, that no
one but the Joyners or another lawyer could even make
out the sense of. Zack and Bob, as everybody owned,
were smart—had always been—and now that they had
learned nearly everything there was to know, they had
come back to town and could hold their own with any
other of the lawyer crew—in fact, could say words as
big and deep and dark as any other lawyer in the world.
And people marveled that the Joyners were their very
own. They themselves had produced the Joyners. Accordingly they felt, not only the humility of awe, but
the pride of ownership and the ecstasy of submission.
Everyone had the satisfaction of knowing that hereafter
if he was going to be eaten by a shark, it would be one
of his own choosing that had grown in native waters.

Zack and Bob, therefore, were now in clover. They
had the inestimable advantage, not only of belonging,
but of being in at the beginning. Before very long they
were enjoying what was practically a monopoly of their
chosen profession and were doing most of the legal
work of the entire mountain region.

It was a curious paradox, though, that these two
brothers, sprung from the same seed, brought up in
exactly the same way, educated to the same degree as
far as formal training went, and set upon the parallel
courses of their lives at precisely the same point, were
to have such widely divergent careers. From the first,

their natures inclined them to seek different objectives.

It was the primary fact of Robert's nature, once he became interested in the law, to study it profoundly, to pierce beyond the letter to the spirit of the thing, and to see it as an adaptive instrument of the common good. Once he had made up his mind to be a lawyer, he concentrated all his fine qualities of character and intellect upon the single goal of making himself into the very best lawyer it was in him to be. From that point on, it never entered his head to want to be anything else.

Zack, however, was never seriously interested in the law. Oh, he wanted to be a lawyer right enough, and as a trial lawyer he became one of the best, with a court-room manner that could sweep a jury completely off its feet even when the weight of evidence was against him. Yes, he wanted to be a lawyer, but he wanted it not because he loved the law, but because he loved something else a great deal more and saw in the law the surest means of getting it. And what Zack really wanted more than anything in life was to be a politician. That was the role he had been born for. All his talents fitted him for it as for nothing else. The law, therefore, was just a stepping stone for Zack, and a very handy one it proved to be.

In the general estimation, even back in the days of their earliest practice together, Robert was always the most respected, the most trusted; but Zachariah was by all odds the most popular, the most loved. And already Zack's feet were firmly planted on the rungs of the political ladder. It did not hurt his chances of success for people to say, as they were now saying: "The man that beats Zack Joyner'll have to git up early and stay up late." He was, throughout his life, the hero of the crowd.

Robert, on the other hand, never played up to an audience. Quiet, blunt, plain-spoken whenever there was need for plain speaking, he was first and last a forthright and an honest man. His purposes he kept forever single, and already those few who knew him

well were predicting for him a useful, and indeed a
noble, career. How useful and how noble, not even they
could have foretold, but it was written in the stars that
such a man as Robert, in a profession which is so frequently besmirched by base and shady uses, could not
fail to distinguish himself upon the bench. And so, in
time, he did, as we shall see.

Meanwhile both brothers married, and chose their
mates well. Robert married rather late in life and had
an only son, who inherited both his father's character
and the delicate sensitivity of his mother. Zachariah,
despite a robust predilection for pretty women, married
young, and he surprised some people by remaining constant to his wife until the end of her days. He became
the devoted father of three lovely daughters, and of a
son in whom he took great pride.

The difference between these two brothers became
more and more marked with the passage of time. And
strange to say, it never brought them into conflict.
Their talents were complementary, and each man respected the other for what he was. For Zack, in spite of
the deliberate charlatanism of speech and manner
which so endeared him to the people, had a solid inner
core of sincerity which even such a completely upright
man as Robert could respect. Thus each was equipped
to fulfill his destiny, but in their later years, even after
Zachariah had risen to the place of highest eminence in
the state, people would still say:

"Zack Joyner will promise you the moon, and you'll
be lucky if you get green cheese. Bob Joyner won't even
promise cheese; but you're likely to get *something* in
the end."

Often those communities which are most ruthless in
their violation of the law are also the most devout in
their respect for it. Of no section has this been truer
than of the South. Almost from the beginning, among
rich and poor alike, the profession of the law has been
esteemed above all others. With people of the wealthier
class, it represented the most approved and honorable

alternative to the other career of plantation agriculture; and, of course, an incomparable advance over the almost ignominious last resort of trade. To the sons of poorer people, the hardy products of small tenantry and the descendants of the mountain whites, it represented an even higher goal—the highest goal they could attain. For, to such people as Zack Joyner, to such people as the more able, fortunate, and intelligent children of old Bear, the law represented almost the only possible means of escape from an environment and from a life that could promise nothing more than the narrow world of backwoods isolation, and the reward of a bare living, hardly gained.

In this way, it came to be accepted almost without question among mountain folk that the most gifted of their sons would, if possible, get into the profession of the law. The lawyer was a kind of medicine man to the community. To his ruder, simpler, and less talented contemporaries, he was the man of learning and of argument, the man of reason and of fluent speech. He was the man to wear good clothes, to have white hands, to live in a good house, and to be vested with the honors and rewards of high authority by his less fortunate fellows, because his talents and accomplishments entitled him to them.

The evil of this system—an evil that has become widespread, rooted in the very structure of the nation's life—is instantly apparent. It offered to many unscrupulous men, under the protections of a high authority, the opportunity to prey upon their neighbors—neighbors who were not endowed with their own shrewdness, smoothness, gift of gab, and formal training, and who, by the conditions of the system, were forced to seek recourse for their troubles from the very men who preyed on them. Not that the lawyers themselves were inevitably and invariably dishonest men. But the system put a high premium on dishonesty, and those lawyers who had integrity enough to resist the ever-present temptation to prey upon their neighbors were, at best,

left in the unhappy position of being themselves a part
of one of the basic functions of society that had been
tainted at its source.

It was very unfortunate that from the beginnings of
American life the profession of the law was commonly
considered, not so much an end in itself, as a means to
an end. And the end to which the law supplied the
means was, in the final analysis, almost identical with
the end of business—namely, personal advantage and
private profit. With business, it did not matter so
much, because, until recently, no one had ever supposed that business had a social purpose as well as
a private one; and this was why, through all human
history, business and trade had been looked down
upon, and the business man condemned by lofty minds
as the stinking, swinking fellow that he usually was.
But the law, in theory at least, was supposed to be
different from this. It represented one of the most elemental of social functions, and if private profit entered
into its operations, this was supposed to be only inci-
dental, in order that lawyers might eat. Actually, matters worked out quite otherwise in practice. Too often
the end to which the law supplied the means was private profit, and the avenue by which one arrived at that
end was politics, party conflict, candidacy, and election
to public office.

In Zachariah Joyner's day, and in his own community, this process was considered so right and so inevitable that any variation from it seemed extraordinary. A
lawyer who did not also "get into politics," or at least
show a partisan and active interest in it, was a queer
fish. So when Robert Joyner decided to stick to the law
and refused to have any truck or traffic with politicians,
people began to wonder about it; and when they could
find no satisfactory explanation of his extraordinary conduct, they shook their heads and said he was a fine
man, of course, but a little queer. There was nothing
queer about Zack. When he began to get into politics
he was doing exactly what everyone naturally expected

him to do. People not only understood, they enthusiasti-
cally approved, and showed their approval by voting for
him the first chance they got.

The course which Zack followed was the accepted
procedure throughout the greater part of the nation. It
is still the standard procedure. And the social implications of this fact are enormous. For, from the very
beginnings of American life, there seems to have been a
general assumption among the majority of the population that the functions of the law and of justice were
divergent, and perhaps quite incompatible and hostile
to each other. This accounted for the grotesque paradox that in such communities as that from which Zachariah Joyner came, where lawlessness, personal violence, and the taking of human life flourished in their
most extreme and savage forms, respect for "the law"
was curiously deep-seated and profound. People in such
communities felt instinctively that justice was a personal matter, and that the ends of justice could only be
individually secured; but that the law was a political
and public matter, and that its purposes and concerns
had better be left as far as possible to the unpredictable
operation of its mysterious machinery.

Thus a man would kill another man to get justice for
himself; but he would go to court to keep from being
hanged for it. Anyone who has ever attended a murder
trial in a mountain community—such a trial as Zack
Joyner attended hundreds of times, and took part in as
counsel for prosecution or defense; such a trial, indeed,
as is still being enacted in Zebulon today—must have
observed the astonishing illustration of this paradox.

A man has killed another man, with whom there has
been "bad blood" for years; and now he is on trial for
his life, and the entire community has come to witness
and take part. On one side, at a rude table, are seated
the attorneys for the state, and the private counsel
which the family of the murdered man has employed to
help the state in the prosecuting of its case. On the other
side, at another similar table, are marshaled the battery
of attorneys which the family of the accused man has

engaged to defend him, and to secure, if possible, a verdict of acquittal.

Behind these two batteries of embattled legal talent, separated from them only by a low wooden barrier, upon the front rows of battered seats, are clustered the many witnesses whom both the prosecution and the defense have summonsed in support of their own arguments—the wives, friends, brothers, children, relatives, and neighbors who have some evidence to contribute. And behind them, crowding the rows of battered seats, packed in the dusty aisles, pressed into the rear four-deep, jammed so thick and dense that they are not able to move in the suffocating atmosphere of mid-July, is as much of the blue-shirted, faded-overalled, and ging-ham-bonneted community as the dingy white-washed room will hold.

In the center, upon a small raised platform, the presiding judge sits at his desk—sometimes a table. To his left is the witness box and the clerk of the court. To his right, the court stenographer. Behind him, tacked to the whitewashed wall, are the Stars and Stripes. And to his left again, upon two rows of chairs, are the twelve men selected for a jury after a three days' inquisition by the contending forces of attorneys: selected from a whole army of veniremen, one hundred in all, such men as these in Zebulon—be-whiskered, overalled, blue-shirted—summonsed and brought in from another county, because everyone in Zebulon, in one fashion or another, is related. In some distant way, even the murdered man is a cousin of the man who sits here now accused of killing him. And the feeling is too high, the passions too fierce—the skein of prejudice, family loyalties, and clannishness; the dense web of more than a hundred years of intermarrying, of conflicts gone but not forgotten, of feuds long past but never dead—it is all too complex and too dangerous to find here a jury that could pass impartial judgment.

The whole thing is as deadly and as thrilling in the naked impact of its social forces as anything on earth can be. The air is electric with its tension; one feels that if a match were struck, the whole place might explode. For everything is here—not only the whole present life of the community, packed, tense, and crowded, stripped down at length to the naked trial of this hour—but the whole history of man is here: his own life, and the life of all his neighbors, the lives of his fathers and his kinsmen and of all who have gone before him.

And with it all, at the very peak and crest of this desperate and final hour, one feels upon all sides, from both groups, among all parties and all partisans, a curious impassivity. Passion leashed there is, the unforgiving will to kill, and kill again, to get full measure of reprisal—an eye for an eye, a tooth for a tooth, a brother for a brother, and a friend for a friend—and yet, with it all, a curious, fatal, deadly impassivity of judgment. For passion belongs to justice, passion shall come later on—and there shall be again a time for justice and vengeance and for blood of murdered men.

But now it is a question of "the law." The law has spoken, the law must have now its full day in court, according to all the devices of its operations, and according to the schedule of its own particular machinery. And these people, every woman, man, and child of them, in this way, in this astounding way, understand, respect, and make a separate place in their own judgment for the law and for its judgments. And in such ways as these, no other folk on earth so deeply understand the law; for, in such ways as these, it has been rooted in their lives, as much a part of them as the very air they breathe, the very speech they speak—yes! the very justice that they take upon themselves and execute, the very vengeance that they so secure.

The trial begins, in such a scene as this—a scene that has not changed an atom since the days when Zachariah Joyner knew it, and took his part in it—a scene which, with all its strange and terrible contradictions, is somehow as memorable and as moving as it is thrilling; for in it, somehow, is the whole enigma of our violent and tormented life—the huge complex of America, with all its innocence and guilt, its justice and its cruelty, its lawlessness and its law.

There at his table sits the judge, a white-haired man, with his string necktie, his boiled shirt, his dark clothes —the quiet vestments of his high authority. Blood of their blood, bone of their bone, kin of their kin—the whole story of their thousand feuds, the knowledge of all their passions and their guilts, together with the very names of each of them, are as familiar to him as the names of his own sons. And he sits in judgment there above the raging furnace of that packed and very quiet hell—not only a man of their own people, but, as the trial proceeds, a man of wisdom and of courage, a splendid and impartial embodiment of law. Here, too, the years have not changed man—for this judge is the same kind of man as Robert Joyner, who sat here, in such trials as these, sixty years ago.

And now the charge is read, the fatal question asked and answered. From the left side of the court, the state rises, and the trial begins. The state's witnesses are called forward. Uneasy, awkward, they shuffle in around the wooden rail—a snag-toothed mountain woman, with a harelip and a bewildered look; a stupid shag-haired fellow with a blunted face; another, small, compact, contained, soft-voiced, with furtive eyes; another, with an uneasy look of divided loyalties; another, grim, determined-looking; some others of this kind; then the murdered man's pregnant wife, large, oily-eyed, and swollen featured—they are all sworn in together, with their right hands dividing three battered books. The first is called into the box; the state Solicitor arises, and the trial is on.

"Where were you on the night of May 14, a little before eight o'clock?" The very words and phrases since Zack Joyner's day have not changed a jot. In kind, not even the Solicitor has changed. This was Zack Joyner's job before him: it's how they begin.

The Solicitor is a young man now, in his mid-thirties, well-made, of something more than middle height—five feet eleven, we should guess—one hundred and eighty pounds of him, abundant, curly hair, by nature crisp, tinged reddish brown. It is a strong face, too, the angles well-defined, high-boned; the jaw strong, competent, jutting out a little; the long lip touched with humor and belligerency—the whole Scotch-Irish, long upper lip more Irish than Scotch. He is already schooled in the manner of the country lawyer, the country politician, still bearing with him traces of high school debate, and subsequent experiments in commencement oratory. He is already able to refer to "the little log cabin where I was born"—or, in somewhat more modern phrase, to "the farm where I grew up."

He's out to get "a good conviction." He admits it. The talk of justice doesn't enter in. A murder has been done—he knows that, so does the other side, and so does everyone. There's no debate in that; it is agreed. The only question now is: "How much?"

The first degree is "out." No one wastes time in talking of the first degree in Zebulon. There hasn't been a conviction in the first degree in Zebulon since before the Civil War. Zack Joyner got that one when he was Solicitor; and it was for rape. There's no first degree for murder out in Zebulon—the only question is: "How much?"

The Solicitor admits he has "a strong side" against him. The murderer is prominent, his family are "big people" in the county; his father back before him killed his man in youth, and his father was a highly respected citizen. The family has stood high, has great connections; to get a conviction will be hard.

Moreover, they have lined up the best murder lawyers that the western districts can provide—the killer's uncle, old man Martin, a good lawyer and a Baptist and a pillar of the church—he "knows the law"; Zeb Pendergraft, the best defense lawyer in the country; Whit Gardiner of Millerton; and several others.

But the long lip, and the smile, good-humored but belligerent, show the Solicitor's belief that he has a chance. It's going to be a hard fight, but he believes he has a chance to get a conviction in the second degree—

from twelve to twenty years—and if he does, another feather in his cap. Twelve years for murder out in Zebulon, added to a mounting record. The pattern of his plan is set: a little later on he'll try the legislature; and after that, we'll see.

It hasn't changed a bit. The man could be Zack Joyner's twin. Even the degrees and stages, the necessary steps, haven't changed a bit since Joyner's day.

And now, the question asked—and from the other side, like an electric flash, the crackle of "Objection!" up and down the line. The leading forward of the witness step by step, the turning over of the witness to the thirsty jackals of the other side. Eyes turn: there is Zeb Pendergraft rocking back and forth in tilted chair, the red eyes and the alcoholic face inflamed and ready now. He tilts back and through his widened knees spits through discolored teeth a dribble of tobacco juice, rocks forward again and comes to rest, and, suddenly, the inflamed face thrust forward, the voice harsh and rasping as a saw, the bully of the murder courts is at his work—the work for which he gets his pay—the work for which he is invariably employed—the work that is his noted specialty.

"*You* know—" compacted equally of tearing rasp and overbearing sneer— "You *know* why you were there! Tell this court why you were there! Tell this court *why* you heard him! . . . Isn't it true that you were there in jail yourself because you'd been arrested for being drunk? . . . You wouldn't *say* that? . . . Well then, what *would* you say? . . . And you don't even know how drunk you were—now, do you? You couldn't even tell this court where you got arrested, could you? . . . You were so drunk you don't even remember where it was now, do you? . . .

"How many times have you been on the chain gang? *Tell* this court how many times you've been on the chain gang. . . . You don't even *know* how many times, do you? . . . You wouldn't *say* that? . . . Well, come on then, and tell this court how many times you *think* it was. . . . Was it four? . . . Or six?

. . . *You wouldn't say?* . . . Well, I'll tell the court.
You've been on the chain gang six times, haven't you?
. . . All told, you've served twenty months upon the
gang—and *you're* here to testify against a man who is
on trial for his life! . . . Why, your honor. . . ."

"Objection!" . . . "Objection sustained!" Or "Objection overruled!" . . . The duel crackles back and
forth like flashes of artillery, the Solicitor tenacious,
truculent, half-grinning; Pendergraft, a series of explosive flashes, a snarling rasp of scalding words, the
inflamed cockerel of the out-thrust head, broken by
deliberate tiltings back at interrupted intervals to shift
his quid and spit deliberately downwards, between widened knees, his dribble of tobacco juice . . . while the
currents of excitement, whispers, and taut interest,
broken by the judge's warning gavel, flash through the
crowd—and while the poor dumb creature, with
stunned face and matted hair, squirms helplessly in his
chair like a hooked fish.

The game goes on; the duel flashes back and forth—
the Solicitor now alert to save the testimony of his chal-
lenged witness:

"Yes, and *tell* the court . . . tell the court just *why*
you were on the chain gang all those times."

And at last, the poor tormented witling has his day:

"Fer gittin' drunk—" and quickly, with an out-jerked
thumb toward Pendergraft—"just like *he* does all the
time."

Then, instant and explosive, an approving roar, a
guffaw of applause, hand-clapping, and the shout of
sympathetic laughter from that overalled, blue-shirted
crowd, as if the heart of simple and tormented man has
found support—the warmth of its own kind against the
thrusts and shrewd outwittings of the law. But the old
judge is on his feet now, his gavel pounding on the
table, his face red beneath his silver shock, with right-
eous wrath:

"If that occurs again, I'll clear the court!   If I
knew who was responsible for this, I'd arrest you all for
contempt of court. . . . Mr. Sheriff, I shall hold you

responsible for any further outbreak or disturbance!
. . . I order you to arrest anyone you see guilty of
such disturbance, and if you have not enough men, I
empower you to appoint deputies!" Sternly, more
quietly, after a moment's pause, almost like a school-
master speaking to a classroom of unruly boys: "This is
a court of law, and a man is on trial here for his life
today! . . . This is a solemn occasion. . . . It is dis-
graceful that any of you should come here to treat it as
if it were a circus!"

The court room is as silent as a tomb now: those
overalled and blue-shirted men almost seem to hold
their breath as the old man with the white hair looks at
them. In a moment, when he sees that they are prop-
erly chastened and subdued, he resumes his seat, adjusts
his spectacles, and says quietly:

"Mr. Solicitor, you may proceed with your examina-
tion."

It is all the same—the same great and thrilling
drama of violence, crime, and human passion, the same
drama of the human community, the great spectacle of
"the law," in the process of its orderly enfoldment—
the rapier duel of embattled wits, the rough-and-ready
school of quick rejoinder, the school of hammer-and-
tongs debate, fighting it out on the dusty floor of a
country court room, in the rough and tumble of a battle for a man's life and liberty—while the whole con-
certed life of the community looks on

It is the same today as it was in Zachariah Joyner's
time. And this is the way he began, the school that
taught him.

CHAPTER V

The Plumed Knight

Theodore Joyner was old Bear's youngest son by his first marriage. As so often happens with the younger children of a self-made man, he got more education than the others. "And," said Zachariah whenever the fact was mentioned, "just *look* at him!" For, mingled with the Joyner reverence for learning, there was an equally hearty contempt among them for those who could not use it for some practical end.

Like his two more able brothers, Theodore had been destined for the law. He followed them to Pine Rock College and had his year of legal training. Then he "took the bar," and failed ingloriously; tried and failed again; and——

"Hell!" old Bear said disgustedly—"hit looked like he wa'nt fit fer nothin' else, so I jest sent him back to school!"

The result was that Theodore returned to Pine Rock for three years more, and finally succeeded in taking his diploma and bachelor's degree. Hence his eventual reputation as the scholar of the family.

Schoolmastering was the trade he turned to now, and, Libya Hill having grown and there being some demand for higher learning, he set up for a "Professor." He "scratched about" among the people he knew—which was everyone, of course—and got twenty or thirty pupils at the start. The tuition was fifteen dollars for the term, which was five months; and he taught them in a frame church.

After a while " 'Fessor Joyner's School," as it was called, grew to such enlargement that Theodore had to move to bigger quarters. His father let him have the hill he owned across the river two miles west of town, and here Theodore built a frame house to live in and another wooden building to serve as a dormitory and classroom. The eminence on which the new school stood had always been known as Hogwart Heights. Theodore did not like the inelegant sound of that, so he rechristened it Joyner Heights, and the school, as befitted its new grandeur, was now named "The Joyner Heights Academy." The people in the town, however, just went on calling the hill Hogwart as they had always done, and to Theodore's intense chagrin they even dubbed the academy Hogwart, too.

In spite of this handicap the school prospered in its modest way. It was by no means a flourishing institution, but as people said, it was a good thing for Theodore. He could not have earned his living at anything else, and the school at least gave him a livelihood. The years passed uneventfully, and Theodore seemed settled forever in the comfortable little groove he had worn for himself.

Then, three years before the outbreak of the Civil War, a startling change occurred. By that time the fever of the approaching conflict was already sweeping through the South, and that fact gave Theodore his great opportunity. He seized it eagerly, and overnight transformed his school into "The Joyner Heights *Military* Academy." By this simple expedient he jumped his enrollment from sixty boys to eighty, and—more important—transmogrified himself from a rustic pedagogue into a military man.

So much is true, so cannot be denied—although Zachariah, in his ribald way, was forever belittling Theodore and his accomplishments. On Zachariah's side it must be admitted that Theodore loved a uniform a good deal better than he wore one; and that he, as Master, with the help of the single instructor who completed the school's faculty, undertook the work of military training, drill, and discipline with an easy confidence which, if not sublime, was rather staggering. But Zachariah *was* unjust.

"I have heard," Zachariah would say in later years, warming up to his subject and assuming the ponderously solemn air that always filled his circle of cronies with delighted anticipation of what was to come— "I have heard that fools rush in where angels fear to tread, but in the case of my brother Theodore, it would be more accurate to say that he *leaps* in where God Almighty crawls! . . . I have seen a good many remarkable examples of military chaos," he continued, "particularly at the outset of the war, when they were trying to teach farm hands and mountain boys the rudiments of the soldier's art in two weeks' time. But I have never seen anything so remarkable as the spectacle of Theodore, assisted by a knock-kneed fellow with the itch, tripping over his sword and falling on his belly every time he tried to instruct twenty-seven pimply boys in the intricacies of squads right."

That was unfair. Not *all*, assuredly, were pimply, and there were more than twenty-seven.

"Theodore," Zack went on with the extravagance that characterized these lapses into humorous loquacity —"Theodore was so short that every time he —— he blew dust in his eyes; and the knock-kneed fellow with the itch was so tall that he had to lay down on his belly to let the moon go by. And somehow they had got their uniforms mixed up, so that Theodore had the one that was meant for the knock-kneed tall fellow, and the knock-kneed tall fellow had on Theodore's. The trousers Theodore was wearing were so baggy at the knees they looked as if a nest of kangaroos had spent the last six months in them, and the knock-kneed fellow's pants were stretched so tight that he looked like a couple of long sausages. In addition to all this, Theodore had a head shaped like a balloon—and about the size of one. The knock-kneed fellow had a peanut for a head. And whoever had mixed up their uniforms had also got their hats exchanged. So every time Theodore reared back and bawled out a command, that small hat he was wearing would pop right off his head into the air, as if it had been shot out of a gun. And when the knock-kneed fellow would repeat the order, the big hat he had on would fall down over his ears and eyes as if someone had thrown a bushel basket over his head, and he would come clawing his way out of it with a bewildered expression on his face, as if to say, 'Where the hell am I, anyway?' . . . They had a devil of a time getting those twenty-seven pimply boys straightened up as straight as they could get—which is to say, about as straight as a row of crooked radishes. Then, when they were all lined up at attention, ready to go, the knock-kneed fellow would be taken with the itch. He'd shudder up and down, and all over, as if someone had dropped a cold worm down his back; he'd twitch and wiggle, and suddenly he'd begin to scratch himself in the behind."

These flights on Zachariah's part were famous. Once launched, his inventive power was enormous. Every fresh extravagance would suggest half a dozen new ones. He was not cruel, but his treatment of his brother bordered on brutality.

The truth of the matter is that the "pimply boys" drilled so hard and earnestly that the grass was beaten bare on the peaceful summit of Hogwart Heights. Uniforms and muskets of a haphazard sort had been provided for them, and all that could be accomplished by a pious reading of the drill manual and a dry history of Napoleonic strategy was done for them by Theodore and his knock-kneed brother in arms. And when war was declared, in April 1861, the entire enrollment of the academy marched away to battle with Theodore at their head.

The trouble between Zachariah and Theodore afterwards was that the war proved to be the great event in Theodore's life, and he never got over it. His existence had been empty and pointless enough before the war, and afterwards, knowing there was nothing left to live for that could possibly match the glories he had seen, he developed rather quickly into the professional warrior, the garrulous hero forever talking of past exploits. This is what annoyed Zachariah more and more as time went on, and he never let a chance go by to puncture Theodore's illusions of grandeur and to take him down a peg or two.

Separate volumes could be written about each member of this remarkable family. A noble biography for Robert, done with a Plutarchian pen—that is what he deserves. A lusty, gusty Rabelaisian chronicle to do justice to the virtues of old Miss Hattie. A stern portrait of Rufus in the Balzac manner. For Zachariah, his own salty memoirs would be the best thing, if he had only thought to write them, for he saw through everybody, himself included; and if he could have been assured that not a word would leak out till his death, so that no political harm could come of it, he would have shamed the devil and told the naked and uproarious truth. As for Theodore—well, we'll try to do our best in the pages of this book, but we know full well beforehand that it won't be good enough for Theodore. No book, no single pen, could ever do for Theodore what should be done for him.

Theodore should have had a group photograph taken of himself. He should have been blocked out by Rubens, painted in his elemental colors by fourteen of Rubens's young men, had his whiskers done by Van Dyke, his light and shade by Rembrandt, his uniform by Velasquez; then if the whole thing might have been gone over by Daumier, and touched up here and there with the satiric pencil of George Belcher, perhaps in the end you might have got a portrait that would reveal, in the colors of life itself, the august personage of Colonel Theodore Joyner, C.S.A.

Theodore rapidly became almost the stock type of the "Southern Colonel-plumed knight" kind of man. By 1870, he had developed a complete vocabulary and mythology of the war—"The Battle of the Clouds," Zachariah termed it. Nothing could be called by its right name. Theodore would never dream of using a plain or common word if he could find a fancy one. The Southern side of the war was always spoken of in a solemn whisper, mixed of phlegm and reverent hoarseness, as "Our Cause." The Confederate flag became "Our Holy Oriflamme—dyed in the royal purple of the heroes' blood." To listen to Theodore tell about the war, one would have thought it had been conducted by several hundred thousand knighted Galahads upon one side, engaged in a struggle to the death against several hundred million villainous and black-hearted rascals, the purpose of said war being the protection "of all that we hold most sacred—the purity of Southern womanhood."

The more completely Theodore emerged as the romantic embodiment of Southern Colonelcy, the more he also came to look the part. He had the great mane of warrior hair, getting grayer and more distinguished-looking as the years went by; he had the bushy eyebrows, the grizzled mustache, and all the rest of it. In speech and tone and manner he was leonine. He moved his head exactly like an old lion, and growled like one, whenever he uttered such proud sentiments as these:

"Little did I dream, sir," he would begin—"little did I *dream*, when I marched out at the head of the Joyner Military Academy—of which the entire enrollment, sir —the *entire* enrollment, had volunteered to a man—all boys in years, yet each breast beating with a hero's heart—one hundred and thirty-seven fine young men, sir—the flower of the South—all under nineteen years of age—think of it, sir!" he growled impressively—"one hundred and thirty-seven under nineteen!——"

"Now wait a minute, Theodore," Zachariah would interpose with a deceptive mildness. "I'm not questioning your veracity, but if my memory is not playing tricks, your facts and figures are a little off."

"What do you mean, sir?" growled Theodore, and peered at him suspiciously. "In what way?"

"Well," said Zachariah calmly, "I don't remember that the enrollment of the academy had risen to any such substantial proportions as you mention by the time the war broke out. One hundred and thirty-seven under nineteen?" he repeated. "Wouldn't you come closer to the truth if you said there were nineteen under one hundred and thirty-seven?"

"Sir—Sir—" said Theodore, breathing heavily and leaning forward in his chair. "Why you—Sir!" he spluttered, and then glared fiercely at his brother and could say no more.

Is it any wonder that fraternal relations between Zack and Theodore were sometimes strained?

To the credit of Theodore's lads, and to the honor of the times and Colonel Joyner's own veracity, let it be admitted here and now that whether there were nineteen or fifty or a hundred and thirty-seven of them, they did march out "to a man," and many of them did not return. For four years and more the grass grew thick and deep on Hogwart Heights: the school was closed, the doors were barred, the windows shuttered.

When the war was over and Theodore came home again, the hill, with its little cluster of buildings, was a desolate sight. The place just hung there stogged in weeds. A few stray cows jangled their melancholy bells and wrenched the coarse, cool grass beneath the oak trees, before the bolted doors. And so the old place stood and stayed for three years more, settling a little deeper into the forgetfulness of dilapidation.

The South was stunned and prostrate now, and Theodore himself was more stunned and prostrate than most of the men who came back from the war. The one bit of purpose he had found in life was swallowed up in the great defeat, and he had no other that could take its place. He did not know what to do with himself. Half-heartedly, he "took the bar" again, and for the third time failed. Then, in 1869, he pulled himself together, and, using money that his brothers loaned him, he repaired the school and opened it anew.

It was a gesture of futility, really—and a symptom of something that was happening all over the South in that bleak decade of poverty and reconstruction. The South lacked money for all the vital things, yet somehow, like other war-struck and war-ravaged communities before it, the South found funds to lay out in tin-soldierism. Pigmy West Points sprang up everywhere, with their attendant claptrap of "Send us the boy, and we'll return you the man." It was a pitiable spectacle to see a great region and a valiant people bedaubing itself with such gimcrack frills and tin-horn fopperies after it had been exhausted and laid waste by the very demon it was making obeisance to. It was as if a group of exhausted farmers with blackened faces, singed whiskers, and lackluster eyes had come staggering back from some tremendous conflagration that had burned their homes and barns and crops right to the ground, and then had bedecked themselves in outlandish garments and started banging on the village gong and crying out: "At last, brothers, we're all members of the fire department!"

Theodore took a new lease on life with the reopening of the Joyner Military Academy. When he first decided to restore the place he thought he could resume his career at the point where the war had broken in upon it, and things would go on as though the war had never been. Then, as his plans took shape and he got more and more into the spirit of the enterprise, his attitude and feelings underwent a subtle change. As the great day for the reopening approached, he knew that it would not be just a resuming of his interrupted career. It would be much better than that. For the war was a heroic fact that could not be denied, and it now seemed to Theodore that in some strange and transcendental way the South had been gloriously triumphant even in defeat, and that he himself had played a decisive part in bringing about this transcendental victory.

Theodore was no more consciously aware of the psychic processes by which he had arrived at this conclusion than were thousands of others all over the South who, at this same time, were coming to the same conclusion themselves. But once the attitude had crystallized and become accepted, it became the point of departure for a whole new rationale of life. Out of it grew a vast mythology of the war—a mythology so universally believed that to doubt its truth was worse than treason. In a curious way, the war became no longer a thing finished and done with, a thing to be put aside and forgotten as belonging to the buried past, but a dead fact recharged with new vitality, and one to be cherished more dearly than life itself. The mythology which this gave rise to acquired in time the force of an almost supernatural sanction. It became a kind of folk-religion. And under its soothing, other-worldly spell, the South began to turn its face away from the hard and ugly realities of daily living that confronted it on every hand, and escaped into the soft dream of vanished glories—imagined glories—glories that had never been.

The first concrete manifestation of all this in Theodore was an inspiration that came to him as he lay in bed the night before the great day when the Joyner Military Academy was to reopen its doors. As he lay there, neither quite awake nor yet asleep, letting his mind shuttle back and forth between remembered exploits on the field of battle and the exciting event scheduled for the morrow, the two objects of his interest became fused: he felt that they were really one, and he saw the military school as belonging to the war, a part of it, a continuation and extension of it into the present, and on down through the long, dim vista of the future. Out of this there flowed instantly into his consciousness a sequence of ringing phrases that brought him as wide awake as the clanging of a bell, and he saw at once that he had invented a perfect slogan for his school. The next day he announced it at the formal convocation.

It is true that Theodore's slogan occasioned a good deal of mirth at his expense when it was repeated all over town with Zachariah's running commentary upon it. The father of a student at the school was one of

Zack's most intimate friends; this man had attended
the convocation, and he told Zack all about it afterwards.

"Theodore," this friend reported, "gave the boys a
rousing new motto to live up to—earned, he said, by
their predecessors on the glorious field of battle. Theodore made such a moving speech about it that he had
all the mothers in tears. You never heard such a blub-
bering in your life. The chorus of snifflings and chok-
ings and blowing of noses almost drowned Theodore
out. It was most impressive."

"I don't doubt it," said Zack. "Theodore always did
have an impressive manner. If he only had the gray
matter that ought to go with it, he'd be a wonder. But
what did he say? What was the motto?"

"*First at Manassas*——"

"First to eat, he means!" said Zachariah.

"*—fightingest at Antietam Creek*——"

"Yes, fightingest to see who could get back first
across the creek!"

"*—and by far the farthest in the Wilderness.*"

"By God, he's right!" shouted Zachariah. "Too far,
in fact, to be of any use to anyone! They thrashed
around all night long, bawling like a herd of cattle and
taking pot-shots at one another in the belief that they
had come upon a company of Grant's infantry. They
had to be gathered together and withdrawn from the
line in order to prevent their total self-destruction. My
brother Theodore," Zachariah went on with obvious
relish, "is the only officer of my acquaintance who performed the remarkable feat of getting completely lost
in an open field, and ordering an attack upon his own
position. . . . His wounds, of course, are honorable, as
he himself will tell you on the slightest provocation—
but he was shot in the behind. So far as I know, he is
the only officer in the history of the Confederacy who
possesses the distinction of having been shot in the seat
of the pants by one of his own sharpshooters, while
stealthily and craftily reconnoitering his own breast-

works in search of any enemy who was at that time nine miles away and marching in the opposite direction!"

From this time on, the best description of Theodore is to say that he "grew" with his academy. The institution thrived in the nostalgic atmosphere that had made its resurrection possible in the first place, and Theodore himself became the personal embodiment of the postwar tradition, a kind of romantic vindication of rebellion, a whole regiment of plumed knights in his own person. And there can be no doubt whatever that he grew to believe it all himself.

According to contemporary accounts, he had been anything but a prepossessing figure when he went off to war, and, if any part of Zachariah's extravagant stories can be believed, anything but a master strategist of arms on the actual field of battle. But with the passage of the years he grew into his role, until at last, in his old age, he looked a perfect specimen of the grizzled warrior.

Long before that, people had stopped laughing at him. No one but Zachariah now dared to question publicly any of Theodore's pronouncements, and Zachariah's irreverence was tolerated only because he was considered to be a privileged person, above the common *mores*. Theodore was now held in universal respect. Thus the youngest of "the Joyner boys"—the one from whom least had been expected—finally came into his own as a kind of sacred symbol.

In Libya Hill during those later years it was to be a familiar spectacle every Monday—the day when the "cadets" enjoyed their holiday in town—to see old Colonel Joyner being conveyed through the streets in an old victoria, driven by an aged Negro in white gloves and a silk hat. The Colonel was always dressed in his old uniform of Confederate gray; he wore his battered old Confederate service hat, and, winter or summer, he was never seen without an old gray cape about his shoulders. He did not loll back among the faded leather cushions of the victoria: he sat bolt upright—and when he got too old to sit bolt upright under his own power, he used a cane to help him.

He would ride through the streets, always sitting soldierly erect, gripping the head of his supporting cane with palsied hands, brown with the blotches of old age, and glowering out to left and right beneath bushy eyebrows of coarse white with kindling glances of his fierce old eyes, at the same time clinching his jaw grimly and working sternly at his lips beneath his close-cropped grizzled mustache. This may have been just the effect of his false teeth, but it suggested to awed little boys that he was muttering warlike epithets. That is what every inch of him seemed to imply, but actually he was only growling out such commands as "Go on, you scoundrel! Go on!" to his aged charioteer, or muttering with fierce scorn as he saw the slovenly postures of his own cadets lounging in drugstore doors:

"Not a whole man among 'em! Look at 'em now! A race of weaklings, hollow-chested and hump-backed—not made of the same stuff their fathers were—not like the crowd we were the day we all marched out to a man—the bravest of the brave, the flower of our youth and our young manhood! One hundred and thirty-seven under nineteen!—Hrumph! Hrumph!—Get along, you scoundrel! Get along!"

CHAPTER VI

The Battle of Hogwart Heights

Theodore had married the year after he reopened the Joyner Military Academy, and everyone agreed at the time that he had made an exceedingly good match. He went to Virginia for his wife. She was Miss Emily Drumgoole, daughter of a Confederate officer, another plumed veteran of the war who, like Theodore, ran a military school, near Winchester. Thus she was also a daughter of the Shenandoah Valley, which had boasted stately houses, courtly manors, and green acres in the days of powdered hair and periwigs, when the wild fastnesses of Zebulon County had been broken only by the moccasin of the Cherokee.

Yes, decidedly, Theodore had done well. His wife was not only a Drumgoole of the Virginia Drumgooles, she was also a lady of quite considerable beauty, flawed only a little by the unfriendly hauteur of a long, cold nose. She came to Catawba in the role of a disdainful invader, and she never dropped the role throughout the remainder of her life.

Being a person of considerable confidence and force, however, she did not spend too much time bemoaning the vanished splendors of her past. Her vision was dominated not so much by the thought of what she had lost as by the calculation of what she was willing now to accept. In her cold, sure way, it was never so much a question of what she was going to take as of what she was going to reject. It was in this frigid frame of mind that she came as Theodore's bride to Hogwart Heights, and settled down there as the glacial monarch of all that she was willing to survey.

And what was she willing to survey? Well, very little, certainly, from the small precincts of Libya Hill.

Robert Joyner and his family she was pleased to welcome among the picked circle of her intimates, for he had been a Brigade Commander in the Civil War and the bosom friend of General Jubal Early—and Jubal Early, like herself, came from Virginia. So when Jubal Early or other great ones came to visit Robert Joyner, she would always invite him to call and bring his guests.

Zachariah was too strong meat for her. She tried to stomach him, but could not, so she coldly turned away. She could not stand his ribaldry and his coarseness. She suspected very shrewdly that in her presence he literally outdid himself in these respects for her special benefit. True, he was a famous man—but in Catawba. He had been Governor of the state—but the state was Catawba. He was now a member of the nation's Senate —but from Catawba. He chewed tobacco and he spat tobacco juice, he made coarse jokes and uttered words that no gentleman would ever utter—all in the presence of a lady. And although he knew much better, and could speak with elegance and beauty when he would, he often deliberately used the language of a backwoods yokel, mentioning with disgusting relish such revolting foods as "hawg and hominy," and delighting in crude anecdotes about how his father had gone barefoot and had never learned to read and write until he was forty years old—this, too, before a lady and her friends.

Miss Hattie Joyner was too much like her celebrated brother in character and plain speaking to find a cordial welcome on the hill. And Rufus, so the lady felt, smelt strongly of his store—a kind of compost of general merchandise, her proud, cold nose informed her, mixed of dry goods and of groceries, and dominated, it seemed to her, by the especial commonness of cheese and calico.

The Joyner clan being thus disposed of, the survivors of her choice were few. She admitted the existence of Dr. Burleigh and his wife and their three mannish and unmarried daughters. He was a dentist, it is true, and dull as dust, but he had come from Charleston and had good connections. The Randolphs also were accepted in her graces. They were Virginia people, and their family was a good one even there.

Her standards of selection were as rigid as the law of the Medes and the Persians, and just as incomprehensible to most of her neighbors; but she knew well enough what they were, and she adhered to them to the end of her days. Wit did not count with her, nor did wisdom, charm, grace, intelligence, character, or any other happy faculty with which men are endowed by nature. The only standard that she had, really, was "family." To her credit be it said that money counted with her not at all. Old Dr. Burleigh was as poor as he was dull. The Randolph fortune was a very meager one. But both of them had "family"—in her own quite definite and restricted meaning of the word. So she received them.

Mrs. Theodore Joyner presented her warlike mate with three offspring, and their arrivals occurred in a sequence almost as rapid as nature would allow. The daughter, Emmaline, was born the year after her parents' marriage. Eleven months later the lady rewarded her delighted spouse with a male heir, who was promptly named Drumgoole to perpetuate the proud accents of his mother's line. The next year she gave birth to her third child, also a boy. The Colonel was secretly a little resentful of the fact that his wife had named the first son, and he claimed for himself the right to name this one; so, after great cogitation and much thumbing of military histories—the only books he ever read—he finally ruled out Hannibal and Quintus Fabius and settled upon Gustavus Adolphus. Mrs. Joyner objected that the boys would call him Gus, but Theodore stood his ground. He pointed out that Dolph had a pleasant sound and was just as easy to say

as Gus, and that Dolph would likely stick if the family
used it, so that is what they called him. And it became
apparent fairly soon that whatever brains and physical
attractions these children were to possess would be
held in almost exclusive monopoly by the last and
youngest of them.

Emmaline grew up under her mother's exacting tutelage, a gawky and unlovely girl, preserved from God-
knows-what contaminations by the proud isolation of
Hogwart Heights. Of her mother's beauty, character,
and personality she inherited nothing except the extravagant snobbishness, as evidenced by the same long, cold
nose. In the course of time she was sent off to the
approved girls' finishing school in Virginia, which, then
as now, was a kind of elegant country club for Southern
maidens—a sanctuary where they could wait till marriage or early spinsterhood claimed them, and meanwhile could fill their empty heads, not with any smattering of conceivably useful knowledge, but with vicious
triviality, gossip, and the accepted rituals and manner-
isms of their own grotesque, aborted little world. The
school was attended by none but born snobs like
Emmaline herself, but most of the others were much
more personable and far more adept than she in the
dreary drivel that has always been held in such high
esteem by the professional representatives of "Southern
charm."

After four years of this, Emmaline was pronounced
"finished" and she returned home again, having learned
all the accents and vocabularies of the approved mode,
but without having found wholly adequate substitutes
for a long nose, a flat bosom, and a small, dull mind.
At twenty-two she was already confirmed, though by no
means reconciled, to a life of unsullied virginity.

Young Drumgoole, or Drum as they called him, was
brought up with the same narrowness of view which his
mother had so painstakingly implanted in his sister.
From the beginning his father had fondly hoped that
the youth would carry on the warlike strain and had
envisioned the proud day when he should be a candi-

date for West Point. And eventually the proud day came, and Drum was sent away into the very heart of the enemy's country with many fond flourishes of fatherly advice and admonition. But it was all to no purpose. He never saw the conclusion of his first term at the great academy on the Hudson. He was a casualty to the rapid fire of trigonometry. He was cut down the first charge. He never even heard the booming of the heavy guns upon the distant front of calculus.

After this, of course, there was nothing left for him to do except to go to Charlottesville and enroll himself among the princelings of the blood at the University of Virginia. Any other alternative was clearly impossible. A gentleman could still attend the United States Military Academy without dishonor, for Lee himself had been a West Point man, but to submit his person to the Yankee degradations of Harvard, Yale, or Princeton was, in the eyes of the Colonel and his wife, unthinkable.

So Drum was sent to Charlottesville as the next-best thing to West Point. Of his life there, there is little to record save that he finally scraped through and learned "to hold his liquor like a gentleman"—which apparently has always been one of the stiffest requirements of the curriculum at that famous university. At length Drum came home again wearing a small blond mustache, and was instantly appointed a Major in his father's celebrated corps, and second in command, the appointment also carrying with it an instructorship in mathematics, trigonometry and calculus included.

If the life of Drum Joyner was the inner seal and signing of his mother's purpose, stamped in wax, then molded outwardly to fit the pattern of his father's wishes, the life of his younger brother, Dolph, was from the outset governed by a purpose of its own. Dolph was one who could have gained and held the coveted honors of West Point training had he so willed, but he would have none of it. He elected to follow Drum to Charlottesville, and his college years showed unmistakable evidence of those qualities which were later to distinguish his whole career.

It is true, he did not shine in scholarship. It is also true, he made no effort to. He was content to pass acceptably, which he had no difficulty in doing, and to leave accomplishments of profounder learning to his more earnest brethren. It was not that Dolph was lacking in earnestness: he possessed it to a degree and in a way that would have astonished his more solemn-seeming contemporaries had they suspected what lay in his mind and heart. It was merely that he already knew of other laurels which seemed to him far more worth winning than any to be found in the academic groves. He had his vision fixed on larger ends. The world, and nothing less, was the oyster of this young Gustavus Adolphus—this young American with the medieval name—and the world had been the mollusk of his desire since childhood.

The geography of western Catawba is especially conducive to the stimulation of visions of the earth. Many writers have spoken of the isolation of these magic hills, the provincial insularity of the mountain man, his remoteness and his consequent asylumage from the affairs and doings of the great and distant world. All of this is true. But the effect of early imprisonment in these hills may lead, in some men, to quite another ending. In the little coves and hollows of the mountain fastnesses of Zebulon County, in the narrow valleys along the rocky creeks that boil down from Clingmans Dome, there may still be found in shack and cabin whole families of people who have never been as far from home as Libya Hill, and for whom the ranging earth beyond the abutment of the mountain at their back is as strange, as alien to all their thoughts and dreams, as Timbuktu. But let the acorn fall on proper earth, or let the lightning strike a chosen rock, and the oak will flourish there, the rock burst forth abundantly with water as it did in Moses' day, and there will be a prophet there to glimpse a Promised Land as golden in its glorious enticements as the one that Moses saw.

Gustavus Adolphus Joyner was the proper earth. Gustavus Adolphus Joyner was the chosen rock. And when the lightning struck, Gustavus Adolphus Joyner was ready there and waiting to receive its flash. When he was a child and looked out from Hogwart Heights and saw the distant ranges of the soaring hills, he did not spend much time in thinking of the coves and hollows hidden away among them, or of the quaint and curious world-forgotten people who grubbed and groped there, from whose own blood and flesh and sinew not so long ago he had himself in partial measure been derived. He looked and saw the hills, and in his kindling vision leaped beyond them. His eyes pierced through the mountain wall and swept beyond to daydreams of the golden cities of the plains.

The very sight of these great hills, under the special enchantments of their weather, the blue haze of their tremendous distances, is like some magic vista of time and the imagined kingdoms of the earth. And there is no place among them that is a better vantage point for this *Weltanschauung* than Hogwart Heights. From the summit of that hill the eye commands a prospect in which grandeur and homeliness are uniquely and wonderfully intermingled, in which the far and the near, the sense of strangeness and utter familiarity, are combined in a single panoramic unity of now and forever. Away to the right, miles distant, sweeping up gradually from the edges of the rolling plateau on which Libya Hill stands, the great ramparts of the Smoky Mountains first appear, ranging westward tier on tier until they end in endlessness that carries the vision on into imagined worlds beyond even after the eye can go no further. To the north, east, and south, more intimate, more friendly and familiar, rise the peaks and undulating masses of the Blue Ridge Mountains.

Before one, and below one, lies Libya Hill, the straggling little town strewn widely on its broad plateau, not always lovely at close hand, but very lovely from the crest of Hogwart Heights. The center of the town, the "business section," looks ghostly, unsubstantial, and unreal under its drifting plumes of soft-coal smoke. But out of the heart of this ethereal-looking town, coming as swift and clean as a deliberate act of cold, clear purpose, bends a bright band of what, beneath the summer sun, seems to be an arc of burnished silver. In a graceful curve it sweeps out from the town and bears around the base of Colonel Joyner's hill, then it winds on westward, sinuously but forever westward, till it is lost among the far-flung, blue-hazed mountains. It is a river, just a thread of river, really, when compared to its great brother, the Tennessee, into which it ultimately flows; yet as rivers go in the Catawba hills, where as a rule they are hardly more than creeks, this one is quite impressive. In August, if the weather has been hot and dry, and all the mountain streams are low, the river at this point below the brow of Hogwart Heights will shrink away from banks of cake-dry mud into a mere trickle. But in the freshets of the spring, or later on in June if rains are heavy and a flood time comes, the river will quickly swell and rise up to the very flooring of the wooden bridge. At these times one understands why the first settlers gave it the curiously haunting name of Catawba Broad.

Here on the summit of this hill, bedded in soft grasses, Dolph Joyner lay a thousand times in childhood and traced the shining river's course as it swept out from the town and wound its way beyond his sight and ken; and with soaring certitude he went on following it, through mountain gorges and deep valleys of verdant coolness, until he came out with it into the imagined world upon the other side, and saw it beckoning on before him in a vision of golden lands.

If others had known why the boy spent so many hours in this solitude of hill-top dreaming, they might have guessed that the little world of Libya Hill and the Hogwart Heights Military Academy would soon prove too small for him. His father, of course, wanted him to pursue what he had come to think of as "the family tradition of arms." It was comforting for the Colonel to think that his two sons would join their talents to carry on the school after he was gone. But this was not to be. For, while Drum was as malleable as putty in his parents' hands, Dolph was made of different stuff.

Rather small of figure, erect and graceful as a shaft, Dolph was quick and hard in both mind and body, but this quickness, this lean hardness, was from childhood couched deceptively in a velvet sheath. He inherited all of the Colonel's courtliness of manner without any of the Colonel's bombast and capacity for self-deception. He seemed to be full of grace and gentleness, and his voice, which was never raised in loudness or in violence, was so pleasing in its quiet modulations that it fell on tired ears or on jangled nerves as gratefully as balm. During his college days at Charlottesville he acquired the nickname of "Silk," which was to cling to him throughout his life. Silk was a perfectly accurate tag for him. His whole personality seemed to be summed up in that one word. But it was silk around iron. It was silk carefully overlaid on flint.

The essential quality of Silk Joyner's character was that he not only always knew the right thing when he saw it, but sensed the right thing before anyone else even suspected its existence. And "the right thing" with Silk Joyner was, simply, the advantageous thing. This was his main concern. His vision of life was utterly utilitarian, and the only utility he recognized was that which applied to himself. He was interested in the usefulness of things and of people only insofar as they could be used to further his own purposes. That suave and courtly figure with the silken voice offended no one unless he had to, but he did not waste himself on useless and unprofitable acquaintances. People who could not help him, who could not profit him in some way, were ruthlessly cast out of his life; but the annihilating act was performed with such smooth courtesy and such winning charm that the luckless victim did not even know he had been kicked out of doors into the cold until he felt the icy blast.

At college, Silk knew precisely the right people, joined precisely the right organizations, made precisely the right connections. He squeezed the whole university life dry of the last drop of nourishment it could offer him, and yet did not once betray the fact to those who knew him best that he was anything else but the infinitely pleasant, polished, charming, friendly, and rather indolent fellow whom they took him to be. He got his law degree at Charlottesville within two years after his graduation from the college, and he followed this with a pleasant and profitable term at Heidelberg.

And then, to cap the climax, he did what no one who knew him could possibly have thought he would ever do. But it was the thing he had always had in the back of his head, the thing that his sure instinct told him was inevitably right, so he did it. He came home— home from his travels, home from Heidelberg, smoother and more silken than he had ever been—and announced that he was going out West, to the Territory of Oklahoma. He said that he was not only going there, but that he intended to settle down there and practice his profession and grow up with the country— there in that raw outpost of civilization which, to his mother's appalled conception, seemed to be as far and wild and grotesquely unfit a place for a gentleman's habitation as an encampment of Sioux Indians.

His mother's tears, his father's entreaties and objurgations, had no more effect upon his purpose than rain against the surface of a cliff. He had made up his mind to go, and go he did. So for the nonce we leave him there, to return to him a little later. In the interim we can be sure of one thing: Silk Joyner is not going to be caught picking daisies out in Oklahoma. While our backs are turned, he will still be cultivating all the right people and doing all the right things, whatever they happen to be in Oklahoma. He will be fitting his silk purse to the sow's ear, and, incidentally, making a very good thing of it.

While Theodore's children were growing up, an event of considerable importance occurred in Libya Hill which, in its sequel, was to reveal as nothing else had

ever done the true mettle of the remarkable woman
who had given them birth. The impact of this event
upon the town was so electrifying that for weeks and
months after the first news of it broke upon the awareness of the natives, they could think and talk of nothing else. Everybody was bursting with excitement over
it, everybody was adither and agog over the stupendous
implications of it, everybody said it was the best thing
that could possibly have happened—everybody, that is,
except Mrs. Theodore Joyner. From the first, she was
totally indifferent to it.

In the late seventies, George Willetts, one of the
richest and most benefactory members of that mighty
tribe of plunderers which has looted the resources of
America for two hundred years, came to Libya Hill
and, after looking over all the mountains in the surrounding region, bought up a whole range of them,
comprising a major portion of three counties, for his
own domain. He imported artists, artisans, and archi-
tects by the hundred, brought in from Italy and the
great cities of the East the most skilled and cunning
craftsmen of their kind—a veritable army of masons,
carpenters, stonecutters, and foresters—and put them
to work creating on his two hundred thousand princely
acres the greatest country house that had yet been built
in all America—the greatest private residence, it was
said, in the whole wide world.

While everybody in town gasped and buzzed with
each new development in this magnificent undertaking,
Mrs. Theodore Joyner sat unmoved on Hogwart
Heights. From her own verandah, on a summer's day,
she sometimes surveyed the proceedings from afar.
Across rolling miles of green plateau she could see from
her hill the Willetts' mansion rising on its hill, a faery
citadel of royal marble gleaming white as alabaster
against the smoky backdrop of the distant mountains,
upborne richly and sustained by swelling masses of green
forest. Poor indeed by comparison was Hogwart Heights
and the weathered paint of Mrs. Joyner's old frame
house. But Mrs. Joyner sat on her verandah and she

never moved. If it ever crossed her mind to draw a comparison, she did so proudly but what she thought she kept entirely to herself and never said a word to anyone.

George Willetts could have owned six counties for all she cared, and built a marble palace of four hundred rooms instead of the two hundred and sixty-two that were now under construction. He could have spent forty million dollars for all she cared, instead of the twenty million that his plans were costing him, and her feeling toward him would have been the same. That is to say, she would have had no feeling toward him. For she had heard that his grandfather had once run a ferry boat. That settled it. He had no "family." He did not belong. As far as Mrs. Joyner was concerned, he did not exist.

The rest of that small world fairly groveled in the dust before the Willetts' name. People fought for a better glimpse of George Willetts' secluded, legendary person when they saw his chrisomed flesh upon the familiar pavements of the town: they pinched themselves to make sure they were not dreaming, so that they could really tell this marvel as a verity to wide-eyed grandchildren sixty years from then. The name of George Willetts and his enchanted domain came to dominate the life of the little town like a magic spell. But through the whole of this, Mrs. Theodore Joyner sat on Hogwart Heights and gave no sign at all.

It is not likely that the Willetts family cared at first. But the years rolled by, the mansion was completed, the Willetts took possession, and as the whole community save the dame on Hogwart Heights sank before them in the obeisance of abject vassalage, the sheer effrontery of the thing began to fascinate them, then to stun them, until finally it overcame them. As time went on, the word was whispered back into the porches of the Willetts' ears that the lady on the Heights had totally ignored them, had shown no interest in their great proceedings, had said, indeed, that Mr. Willetts had no "family," and that she—God save the mark! —the lady on Hogwart Heights, the mistress of a

shabby house and of a one-horse military school—
would not receive them!

It was funny. It was unbelievable. It was absurd. It
was—it was—it was—great God! it was simply horrible,
that's what it was! It was not to be endured! It had
never before happened to a member of the Willetts
family, and it had to stop!

The upshot of it was that there came a day—a
memorable, never-to-be-forgotten day—when the Willetts family did what it had never done before. It put
its pride into its pocket and went to call upon a total
stranger—and to make the circumstance still more incredible, if that can be, a total stranger who had
snubbed the Willetts family dead and cold.

History does not record that on that memorable day
the bells were rung backward, or the flags hung at half
mast in Libya Hill, or the streets lined with silent
throngs, their heads uncovered, as Mrs. Willetts drove
through town on her way to Hogwart Heights. There is
a rumor that there was a partial eclipse of the sun, but
scientific research does not confirm it. Still, everyone
who remembers anything about it agrees that it was a
day of days.

The coronation of a king may be witnessed by the
populace, but the solemn investiture of the royal robes
is reserved for the royal family and members of the most
select nobility. Accordingly the full and satisfying record of what happened on that famous day will always
be concealed somewhat in mystery. Yet rumor, like a
fine and subtle smoke, can insinuate itself through solid
walls, and rumor whispers that upon that day Mrs.
Willetts got up at the crack of dawn—a thing unknown to her before—and ate the lightest kind of breakfast. Henchmen of the royal preserve, game wardens,
foresters, French maids, and such like folk were known
to have hinted discreetly afterwards that on this day
Mrs. Willetts was not utterly herself. She looked pale
and haggard in the mirror, her small, jeweled hand was
seen to tremble slightly as she put the cup back on the
tray, she is said to have called for her smelling salts and

to have taken two sharp sniffs, one more than was her customary average.

Driving down along the eight miles of lovely road that wound from the mansion to the lodge gates of the great estate, behind a pair of spanking bays, two liveried coachmen perched above her, and two more with folded arms behind, in a princely equipage of which the very harness studs were solid silver, the lady was said to have betrayed the tension of her nerves, the agitation of her mind, by the way in which she twirled the handle of her parasol with one small gloved hand and nervously kept clenching and unclenching the fingers of the other. She swept through the arches of the lodge gate with set and rigid features, and for the first time in her life failed to respond with her customary gracious little nod and smile to the bows of the venerable retainer who kept the gate.

These symptoms of internal stress were likewise noted by the populace as Mrs. Willetts passed through town. At a spanking trot the splendid carriage swept smoothly through the streets on velvet wheels. The sun was shining and the silver harness sparkled like a maiden's dream. The flowers were blooming, the month was May, the laughter of young children and of lovers could be heard upon the air. All nature wore a smile that day, but Mrs. Willetts did not smile. Her face was rigid and her eyes were blank. Had she been carved of stone she could not have been more preoccupied, more unaware of all the eyes, the hats, the faces, and the smiles that were raised hopefully to her in greeting.

The carriage swept smartly up South Main Street, turned the corner into College at the Square, rolled out College to Montgomery, trotted swiftly down the long slope of Montgomery to the bottom, then up the hill beyond and out of town. Dust arose now beneath those shining hooves, dust arose around that shining equipage, around the coachmen and the footmen and the flunkeys; dust swirled up around the fashionable figure of George Willetts' wife, obscuring her designs and purposes, clouding all her hopes, smothering what-

ever thoughts she had been thinking. At last the carriage crossed the old wooden bridge that spanned the
river at the base of Hogwart Heights and heaved up as
it struck a bump upon the other side. It lurched into
the rutted and uneven roadway that wound up around
the hill to the academy, and then, still toiling and
lurching upward, disappeared from sight around a
bend.

Mrs. Willetts finally arrived, got out, mounted the
wooden steps to the verandah, and there, straight and
cold at journey's end, stood Mrs. Theodore Joyner.
They went into the house together—and the rest is
silence. Only Rumor knows what happened then, and
Rumor was not slow to tell it.

They are supposed to have had tea together, and it is
said that for some moments neither spoke a word.
Then after a long and painful silence Mrs. Willetts
remarked that she had heard so much of Mrs. Joyner
and had looked forward to this meeting for quite some
time.

Mrs. Joyner, after a perceptible pause, replied: "You
are a stranger in this part of the country, I believe?"

Mrs. Willetts strove to assimilate the meaning of this
question, and is said to have gasped a little and finally
to have managed: "Yes—I—I—I suppose I am. We
have been here just six years."

This information was received with another long and
attentive silence.

Finally Mrs. Willetts said: "I—I do hope you will
come to see us soon."

Mrs. Joyner inclined her head ever so slightly in a
gesture that was committal of nothing, and, without
answering directly the lady's invitation, is rumored to
have said: "I believe you and your husband are both
Northern people, are you not?"

"Yes—" Mrs. Willetts blurted out—"but my grand-
mother was a Southern woman."

"Of what family?" Mrs. Joyner asked with an accent
of sharp interest.

"Of the Marsden family—" Mrs. Willetts answered quickly—"the Marsden family of Virginia."

"Which branch?" Mrs. Joyner asked with glacial sternness. "The Southwestern or the Tidewater?"

"The Tidewater," Mrs. Willetts cried out with almost desperate hopefulness.

Mrs. Joyner inclined her head ever so slightly and said, "Ah!"

It is not to be supposed for a moment that this "Ah!" was a warm "Ah!"—an "Ah!" of friendly surrender. It was no such "Ah!" as this at all. But it is reported that there was in it just a perceptible relenting into interest, a suggestion that a very mild thaw had set in, an indication that here at last was something that could be taken into consideration and examined seriously.

"And your mother?" Mrs. Joyner now said, as she put down her cup. "Was she a Southern woman, too?"

"No," Mrs. Willetts answered somewhat wretchedly, "she—she was a Northern woman." Here Mrs. Joyner is said to have stiffened visibly again, and Mrs. Willetts rushed on recklessly: "But she was a Dyckman—a New York Dyckman."

"Was that one of the Dutch families?" Mrs. Joyner asked sharply.

"Yes, one of the very first Dutch families. I do assure you, one of the very oldest Dutch families!"

Mrs. Joyner said nothing for a moment, then, taking up her saucer and teacup again, she remarked with the first faint flush of condescension in her voice: "I have heard that there are some very good Dutch families."

Here Mrs. Joyner sipped her tea, and carefully put cup and saucer down again, and Mrs. Willetts is said to have heaved a long, slow, and quite audible sigh of relief.

Finally Mrs. Joyner spoke again. "I should be glad," she said, smiling graciously as she framed the words, "to come to see you when I am next in town."

CHAPTER VII

A Stranger Whose Sermon Was Brick

Fifty years ago, one of the most extraordinary people in the town of Libya Hill was a man named Webber. In a great many curious and interesting ways which no one could have foreseen, he was destined to influence the life of the whole town. John Webber came to Libya Hill in 1881, and since the story of his arrival there involved the celebrated Zachariah Joyner, it attained a considerable local notoriety.

It was in the autumn—early October—of 1881. Judge Robert Joyner, Zachariah's brother, had gone to Millerton, twenty-four miles away, to attend the session of the Circuit Court which was being held there at the time. Zachariah had been in Washington, and on the way back had stopped to meet his brother in Millerton.

Millerton was as far as the railroad went in those days. The line had not yet reached Libya Hill, but it was under construction at the time. The building of this particular stretch of the railroad was a tremendous job of engineering for those days. As anyone can see who rides over it today, the line winds back and forth with corkscrew bends and hairpin turns for eight miles between Millerton at the base of the mountains and Ridgepole Gap at the crest, some fourteen hundred feet above. It is a beautiful and thrilling ride—one of the most beautiful in America—and there are places where one can see the track below one seven times.

In 1881, all of this was in the process of

construction. The crews were just finishing the grading of the right of way: the tracks were laid, and work cars and shifting engines were already moving over them, but there were no scheduled trains. To get to Libya Hill people had to take the stage. It left Millerton every afternoon at one o'clock and reached Libya Hill at six, which was not bad time considering the tremendous pull and climb of those first eight miles.

The stage wasn't much of a contraption, judged by romantic or Wild Western standards. It was just a wagon with seats for six people, and it was drawn by two horses. When it rained, the dirt road winding up around the mountainside to Ridgepole Gap became a swamp of sticky mire. And usually, when this happened, the passengers got out and walked.

On this day, Zack Joyner had come down from Washington on the train which arrived in Millerton at noon. He and his brother had dinner at a place called Crandall's Tavern, which was a country hotel from which the stage departed. The man Webber had himself arrived on the same train. Zachariah had noticed him, and while they were eating at the tavern Zack commented to his brother on the stranger's peculiar appearance. Afterwards Webber got in the stage with them, and almost immediately Zack, as was his custom with anyone whose appearance interested him, struck up a conversation.

The stage had three rows of seats. In front was the driver's seat, with room for one passenger beside him; behind this and backing up against it was the second seat, and facing the second was a third. There were only five passengers that trip. Judge Robert Joyner sat up front beside the driver, Zack sat behind the driver facing Webber on the left side of the coach, and there were two ladies, a mother and her daughter, who were going as far as Ridgepole Gap.

Zachariah started off at once in his usual way. Webber did not know who he was, but the other people did. In a few minutes he had them laughing at his jokes, and Webber was looking at him with a kind of puzzled grin. Presently Zack asked Webber where he was bound for and if he was a stranger in those parts, knowing full well that he was. Webber answered that he had never been in Old Catawba before and said that he was bound for Libya Hill. Still curious, Zack asked him if he was not "a Northern man." Webber said he was, and that he came from Pennsylvania.

The stranger had answered these questions readily enough but had volunteered no additional information about himself, so Zack now asked him if he was on a visit. Webber said no, that he was a brick mason and general builder, and that he was coming to Libya Hill to take charge of work on the new hotel which the Corcorans were putting up on Belmont Hill, in the center of the town, and for which ground had already been broken. Zack had already concluded that the man was a laborer of some sort, for his hands were thick and strong and had the look of having known much hard work; and Zack had also noticed on the index finger of the man's right hand a horny callous, which Zack now took to be the mark of persistent wielding of the trowel. Even in later years, when Webber became prosperous and confined himself to superintending the labor of others, this callous remained, and one always felt it in shaking hands with him.

The news of his occupation and purpose was received by everyone with considerable interest and satisfaction. The Corcorans were rich people who had recently come into that section and bought up tracts of property and laid out plans for large enterprises, of which the hotel was the central one. And only a few years before, George Willetts, the great Northern millionaire, had built and moved into his fabulous country estate near by. New people were coming to town all the time, new faces were being seen upon the streets. And now that the railroad would soon be opened, there was a general feeling in the air that great events were just around the corner for them all, and that an important destiny was in store for Libya Hill.

It was the time when they were just hatching from

the shell, when the place was changing from a little isolated mountain village, lost to the world, with its few thousand native population, to a briskly-moving modern town, with railway connections to all parts, and with a growing population of wealthy people who had heard about the beauties of the setting and were coming there to live. It was, in fact, the beginning of their "boom"—a boom which at times was to lapse, to lie dormant, but never to die out utterly until the final explosion fifty years later. People had already begun to learn the language and to talk the jargon with a practiced tongue. Even then one was hearing a great deal about the beautiful scenery, the magnificent climate, the purity of the crystal water. The whole vocabulary of the tourist community was just waiting to be translated into the lush phrases of the professional rhapsodist and the Chamber of Commerce guide.

Zachariah Joyner assured the stranger that he was coming to "the greatest country in the world," and enlarged upon the theme in the syllables of the ornate rhetoric of which he was a master. What Webber said is not on record, but it can be assumed from his character that his comment was bluntly noncommittal, quiet, to the point.

The talk then turned to travel and to railway journeys, which in those days were considerably more complicated and difficult than they are now. Webber remarked that he had come all the way from Baltimore, that the trip had been a long and wearing one, with many changes, and that he would be glad when it was over because he was pretty tired. Zachariah then told a story about "Greasy" Wray, a country lawyer out in Zebulon whom Joyner had appointed a Circuit Judge during his first term as Governor. Greasy Wray had never been anywhere, and when he received his first instructions to hold court in Harrington, a seacoast town four hundred miles away, he was delighted at the prospect of seeing so much of the world and proceeded at once to heed the call of civic duty. He set out on horseback to Libya Hill; then he went by stage to Millerton; then by the Exeter and West Catawba Railway to Exeter; then by the Belmont, Fletcher, and West Central to Sanderson; then by the Sanderson and Northeastern to Dover; then by the Dover and Mount Arthur to Redfern; then by the Redfern and Eastern Shore to Bellamy, where, all exhausted from his three-day journey, he arrived to find the boat waiting. Greasy Wray got on board at once and went to sleep, and woke up the next morning to find the boat docked at its destination. He saw a great crowd of Negroes on the wharf, went ashore and hired a hack, was driven to a hotel, and demanded of the astounded clerk that the sheriff be sent for right away. Fifteen minutes later he welcomed the no less astounded sheriff in his room and said: "I am Judge Wray of Zebulon, and I have been sent here to open court in Harrington." The sheriff was speechless for a moment, then he replied: "Hell, man, this ain't Harrington. It's *Baltimore!*"

This story was one of Zachariah's favorites, and he told it with gusto. He was off to a good start now, and as the stage toiled up the mountainside the stories rolled from him in a swelling tide. Just before the stage reached Ridgepole Gap, on the last bend of the road as the team pulled toward the crest, the wheels lurched down into a heavy rut. The two women were almost tossed out of their seats. They screamed, and then, as the team pulled out of it again, one of the ladies turned to Zachariah and, giggling apprehensively, remarked:

"Oh, Senator! I do declare! It seems as if all the holes are on our side!"

"Yes, madam," Zachariah boomed out gallantly and without a moment's hesitation, "and all the roots on ours."

His face did not change expression as he spoke these words, nor his blue eyes lose a vestige of their innocence. But Robert Joyner had to take vigorous recourse to his handkerchief and blow his nose loudly for some time; and when he finally looked back, Zachariah was blandly surveying the landscape, while Webber was staring rigidly out across the side of the stage, and his thick neck and ruddy face were purple.

The ladies got out at Ridgepole Gap, and from that point on Zack Joyner gave free play to his bawdy vein. He asked Webber where he planned to stay when he got to town. Webber said he didn't know, but supposed there was a boarding house or a hotel.

"Well," said Zachariah gravely, "I usually put up at Joyner's place myself."

Mr. Webber very innocently inquired: "Is that a good place?"

"Yes," said Zachariah. "Taking it all in all it suits me about as well as any place I've found. You get a good bed and good accommodation there, and Mrs. Joyner's known as one of the best cooks in these parts. And say—" here Zack looked around slyly, then leaned forward, and, tapping Webber on the knee, said confidentially—"she's not a bad-looking woman either. As a matter of fact—" again he looked round slyly— "when I go there, I usually sleep with her."

It was shameless and outrageous, but it was Zack Joyner, too. One look, however, at John Webber's astounded face was too much for Zack. He burst into a roar of laughter, in which the driver and Judge Robert Joyner joined, and then he introduced himself.

Just after this the thing happened. The stage came to a little rise where the road crossed the right of way of the new railroad tracks. The crews were working here. Just as the team pulled up to the crossing, a shifting engine with a string of dump carts came by. The horses reared and snorted, and the driver lashed them with his whip. Then the train clanked past, the horses pulled skittishly across the tracks, the engine whistled—and the horses ran away.

The team plunged down the mountain road at breakneck speed. The driver clamped his foot upon the brake, the brake rod snapped, and as they neared the bend, Judge Robert Joyner reached over, grabbed the reins, and swerved the team around. The stage skidded to one side and almost overturned, and Zachariah pitched out on his head. Judge Robert Joyner and John Webber bent over him while the driver pulled the team around. His head had struck a rock, and there was a great blue swelling on his forehead. They opened his collar and his shirt, chafed his wrists, and spoke to him. He didn't stir. Robert said he thought Zack was a dead man, because his eyelids were half open and his eyeballs looked like glass.

Then Webber got up, went over to the stage, spoke to the driver, reached in underneath the seat, and pulled out a bottle of Glover's Mange Cure. He came back, uncorked the bottle, bent over Zack, forced the bottle neck between his lips, and poured its contents down his throat.

Robert said later that if Webber had held a blowtorch to Zack's behind, the effect could not have been more instantaneous. He did not *get* up, big, heavy man that he was—he *rose* up, shot up into the air as if he had been fired out of a gun.

"Great God!" he roared. "You've burnt me up!"

That was the way John Webber came to town.

The story lost nothing in the telling that Zachariah gave it, so that in no time at all John Webber became known to everyone as "the man who burnt Zack Joyner up." And the story typified the man: the stark remedy and the blunt, unspoken way in which he administered it were characteristic of everything he ever did. And, most characteristic of all, as Zack himself was the first to admit, was the fact that "it worked." That was the beginning of the sound respect that both Zack Joyner and his brother Robert had for Mr. Webber throughout the remainder of their lives.

Although there was undoubtedly a touch of the grotesque in his appearance, one forgot it quickly on acquaintance, because of the natural dignity—the sheer animal dignity—of the man. For one thing, John Webber never in his life felt a moment's embarrassment be-

cause of the way he looked. He was certainly not vain of
his appearance: he was the last person in the world to
deceive himself. He would even laugh good-naturedly
and say: "No one's ever going to give me the prize for
beauty at the county fair, and no matter—I've got to
work for *my* living, anyway." But he was not ashamed,
either. He could resent an insult or an affront to his
self-respect as quickly as any man, but he was entirely
without morbid sensitivity. He accepted the well-inten-
tioned but sometimes rather crude jokes of his fellows
with quiet amusement, and could even turn a joke
against a man as well as enjoy one at his own expense.

The wise thing about his attitude was that he accepted his appearance sensibly and without self-con-
sciousness. "I'm not much for looks," he would say,
"but I've no complaint to make. I've always had a good
constitution, and that was lucky, because I've had to
work hard all my life, ever since I was twelve years old.
I've had my share of the hard knocks, I can assure you,
and done my share of the hard labor; so even if I'm no
parlor beauty I guess I can still be pretty thankful that
I was strong enough to stand up and take the hard
knocks as fast as they came." This innate dignity of the
man enabled him to keep at all times what other people
sometimes lost—his own self-respect.

Judge Robert Joyner used to say that if Webber had
been "an educated man" he could have "gone far in
the world"—a statement which he would conclude emphatically by saying: "He would have made a fine lawyer." Judge Joyner's only son, Edward, first heard his
father say these words when he could not have been
more than twelve years old. He never forgot them, and
later on it struck him as curious that he should have
remembered them at all. Ordinarily a boy of that age is
not very much concerned with the merits of the gentlemen who either adorn or might have adorned the legal
profession—even when one's father is a lawyer, and a
judge of the Circuit Court to boot. Young Edward
Joyner was certainly no different from most other boys

in this respect. He was interested in a great number of things at that time, but the law was emphatically not one of them.

Among the things that did interest young Edward Joyner was the circus. He saw his first circus some six months after Mr. Webber arrived in town, and at the same time caught his first glimpse of Mr. Webber. Perhaps that is why he remembered Mr. Webber and his father's opinion of him—why, indeed, Mr. Webber and the circus became interfused in his mind forever after— because he would never forget how Mr. Webber helped the circus come to town. From that time on, young Edward Joyner was pretty well convinced, like his father, that John Webber could do anything he attempted, and do it well.

This great event concerned a very modest version of Barnum's Mammoth Circus and Combined Shows. Since the last stretch of the new railroad was still under construction, the whole thing had been brought in by wagon across the mountains all the way from Millerton. They even had an elephant named Jumbo, and they had marched him up across the Blue Ridge, too—and it was just like Hannibal crossing the Alps. And as Edward Joyner later remembered it, one of the things he wanted to be at that time, and for a long time afterwards, was the man who sat on Jumbo's skull and rode up across the mountains; and if he could not be that man, then he was willing to be that man's man—or his boy or his apprentice—or his valet—or his valet's man—or to take any office, however humble, that the retinue of such a princely officer could furnish—and then, of course, work his way up from there.

It was the spring of the year. The snows were melting in the mountains and the river had flooded the bottoms. The big circus vans, coming into town, had mired up on the river road a mile or two away and were stuck there in the mud up to the axle hubs. The circus people tried to get the vans out of the mud. It was a hard job, they had more than they could do, and they sent out calls for teamsters. Mr. Webber had two teams of iron-gray mules which he used for hauling: he rented them to the circus men that morning and came along himself to see that they got handled right.

It was Sunday morning. The weather had cleared after a week of rain and it was one of the first fine days of April. Judge Joyner and his son had hitched up the buggy and driven out to see the fun, and when they got there it seemed to the boy that everyone in town had come out to meet the circus. They found that part of the circus procession had gotten through all right, but the rest of it was stuck in the mud, with the circus people standing around the vans, cursing, cracking their whips at the big, straining horses, and making no progress whatever. They might as well have tried to pull those heavy vans out of the Everglades. Like Mercutio's wound, the mudhole in the road may not have been as deep as a well or as wide as a barn door, but it served, and the vans and wagons which had already managed to traverse it successfully had churned it up into something resembling the consistency of liquid glue.

So the horses tugged and strained, the circus people cracked their whips and cursed, the whole town looked on and marveled—the sunshine and the hills were the same as they had always been in April—and the big vans never budged. At this moment Mr. Webber arrived from town with two wagonloads of lumber and his four gray mules.

It was the first time the boy had ever seen him. When we are children, our initial impression of a man is likely to color everything we feel about him the rest of our lives, and certainly young Edward Joyner could have had no better introduction to the sharp and strong excitement of Mr. Webber's personality than he had on that bright morning. Everything about the bizarre situation—all so new and strange to the boy—with the brightly painted circus wagons and the big horses lined up along the road, the shining and enchanting day with every leaf still a-sparkle with the rain, and the rocky river, flooded to its muddy rim as he had never seen it before, rushing along with a full and almost soundless violence, and carrying with it the heavy, wet, and rotten, yet curiously fresh and pungent, smell of vegetation—all this gave to the occasion the thrill of a strange and wonderful excitement, as sharp and piercing as a blade.

Mr. Webber as he first appeared on the scene was one of the most extraordinary-looking people that young Edward Joyner had ever seen in his whole life. And this, apparently, was also the verdict of the crowd. As he came up, a kind of involuntary snort or gasp of laughter—more of sheer astonishment than anything else—rose upon the Sunday morning air. The little boys giggled, and Edward heard a man behind him saying softly, in a tone of wonder:

"Hell, I knew they had an elephant—but somebody must have left the monkey cage unlocked!"

At this remark, almost unpremeditated in its humor, there was louder and more open laughter, a growing wave of it throughout the crowd.

John Webber stood there on his wagonload of lumber, and, seen from below as the others had to look up at him, he did seem to fit the man's remark. Although he was somewhat above the average height, being about five feet ten inches tall, he gave the curious impression of being inches shorter. This came from a variety of causes, chief of which was a slightly "bowed" formation of his body. At first sight there was something distinctly simian in his short legs, bowed a little outward, his large, flat-looking feet, the powerful, barrel-like torso, and the tremendous gorilla-like length of his arms, with the huge paws dangling almost even with his knees. He had a thick, short neck that seemed to sink right down into the burly shoulders, and close sandy-reddish hair that grew down almost to the edges of the cheek bones and to just an inch or so above the eyes. His eyebrows were extremely thick and bushy, and he had the trick of peering out from under them with head out-thrust in an attitude of intensely still attentiveness. His nose was short, pointed, and turned up so sharply at the end that the nostrils almost seemed to flare; and consequently, he had an extremely long and simian upper lip. What was most startling of all, perhaps, was the extraordinary smallness—the extraordinary delicacy—of the features when contrasted with the power and weight of the big torso.

His costume on that sparkling Sunday morning was also remarkable. He was wearing his "good Sunday clothes." It was a suit of black broadcloth, heavy and well cut, the coat half cutaway, a stiff white shirt with starched cuffs, a wing collar with a cravat of black silk tied in a thick knot, and a remarkable-looking derby hat, pearl-gray in color and of a squarish cut. As he stood on his wagonload of lumber, he took off the hat and scratched his head thoughtfully, revealing as he did so that his sandy-reddish hair was thin on top, with a wide bald swathe right down the center of his skull.

It was at this instant that the crowd laughed. John Webber paid no attention. One would have thought that he did not hear the laughter, so unself-conscious was the dignity of his attitude, and almost instantly the crowd's disposition to laugh at him died out. He continued to survey the scene a moment, attentively and quietly, then got down off his wagon and said to one of the circus people:

"Take your horses out of the traces."

This was quickly done. The big horses were unhitched and plodded jangling down the road.

"Now," said Mr. Webber to his own teamsters, "unhitch those mules."

This was also done.

"You'd better let us use our horses," one of the circus people said. "We know how to handle horses."

"I know how to handle mules," said Mr. Webber. "Give me six of your men and help unload the lumber from my wagons."

The lumber was unloaded. In just a few minutes Mr. Webber had shored some stout timbers down into that sea of glue and got his two mule teams hitched up to the leading van; the big mules braced their muscles, strained, and the big van heaved up out of the mudhole and lurched forward onto solid earth.

Then Mr. Webber began to use the rest of his lumber. In a wonderfully short time, under his direction, the men had laid down a bridge across that treacherous sink, and one by one the big circus vans rolled forward and over it to safety.

Later, Mr. Webber came over to the buggy where Edward and his father sat, and stood for a moment talking to Judge Joyner. Edward noticed that the man's good Sunday clothes were now spattered with mud, and that his big hand, as he rested it upon the buggy seat, was also caked with mud; but Mr. Webber seemed not to notice it at all. He just stood there talking quietly, as if such events as this were all in the day's work and must be taken as they came. Of what was said, the boy had no clear recollection later, except that Judge Joyner made some observation about the poor condition of the road, and that Mr. Webber, after looking at the slough again, shook his head with a short, strong movement, and said bluntly:

"We have pikes in Pennsylvania that have been good a hundred years."

Then he turned and walked away. And Judge Robert Joyner, as he gathered up the reins, said quietly to his son:

"There goes a very remarkable man."

It must have been only a month or two after this when young Edward saw the man again. Certainly it was that same year. Since the cornerstone of Judge Robert Joyner's old law office bears the date 1882, it is easy enough to fix the time.

Edward came out of the house one morning about nine o'clock and found Mr. Webber talking with his father in the yard.

"Now, Mr. Webber," he heard his father say, "what I have in mind is this: an office big enough for two good-sized rooms, one for my clerk and for any people who may be kept waiting, and one for my private use. I thought we'd put it about here—" he indicated the upper corner of the yard. "That would be, say, about twenty feet across, and about so deep—" he paced off the distance to which he thought the structure might extend. "Now, it's not going to be anything very fancy. I'm not even going to have an architect draw up the plans. I've sketched them out myself, and I think they will do. But what I had in mind was something plain and substantial, and I'd like to get an estimate from you on the cost."

"What material do you want to use?" asked Mr. Webber.

"Why—" Judge Joyner looked puzzled for a moment, then, glancing back toward the rambling gables of his house, with its clapboard covering, he said— "something like the house there, I suppose. Wouldn't you use pine?"

"No, sir," Mr. Webber answered firmly. "I'd build it with brick."

Young Edward was looking at Mr. Webber when he said this, and now for the first time it occurred to the boy that Mr. Webber was somewhat like a brick himself: the squat figure, the powerful shoulders, the thick neck, the red-weathered face, and the bald head, all had a compact solidity and coloring that suggested that he might be shaped from the materials in which he dealt. To the boy the idea seemed sensational and exciting. Mr. Webber's words surprised his father, too, for it had not occurred to him to use brick; and for a moment, while Mr. Webber waited stolidly, Judge Joyner was silent. Then, rather doubtfully, as if he were not sure he had heard a-right, he said:

"Brick?"

"Yes, sir," said Mr. Webber inflexibly, "brick. It's not going to cost you so much more than lumber by the time you're done, and," he went on quietly, and with conviction, "it's the only way to build. You can't rot it out. You can't rattle it or shake it. You can't kick holes in it. It will keep you warm in winter and cool in summer. And fifty years from now, or a hundred for

that matter, it will still be here. I don't like lumber,"
Mr. Webber continued doggedly. "I don't like wooden
houses. I come from Pennsylvania"—ah, there it was
again!—"where they know how to build. Why," said
Mr. Webber, with one of his rare displays of boastful-
ness, "we've got stone barns up there that are built
better and will last longer than any house you've got in
this whole section of the country. In my opinion there
are only two materials for a house—stone or brick.
And if I had my way," he added a trifle grimly, "that's
how I'd build all of them."

The idea, once planted in Judge Joyner's mind, took
firm root. So brick it was. Ground was broken for the
office within a month, and before the summer was over
the place was built and the Judge had moved into it.

And it's there yet, in between the corner filling station and the dilapidation of the old frame house, which
now functions dismally as a "tourist home." The old
office is still there, squat, blunt, rusty-looking, certainly
not an architectural triumph, but living up in every
respect to the specifications that John Webber laid
down almost sixty years ago. Amid the wreckage of
Libya Hill's recent boom it stands as a substantial survi-
vor of an earlier time, a token that someone was here
who believed in making things to last.

From that moment on, young Edward's memory of
John Webber was tied up with brick. Also from that
time on, the appearance of the town began to change,
to take on here and there a more substantial look. And
John Webber was himself so much the cause and agent
of that change that if his whole life story, his epitaph,
had to be written in eight words, there could be no
better one than:

"Here lies a man who believed in brick."

CHAPTER VIII

The Dead World Relived

Young Edward Joyner's own view of things was beginning to change about this time. Probably it would have
changed anyway in the course of events, but because
the impressions of boyhood are so influenced by personality, the whole change which was going on in him was
always later to be identified with John Webber. Webber arrived in town just at the time when the old order
was "yielding place to new"—when new forces and new
faces were coming in, when the townspeople's thoughts
and visionings were going *out*, when the town was first
establishing its connections with the world. And because Webber was coincident with that process—indeed, did so much himself to fashion it—he always
stood, in Edward Joyner's memory, as the incarnation
of it.

Later, as he looked back upon his childhood, there
was a kind of geographic dividing line which separated
his conception of the world into two periods. It was a
kind of Before Webber and After Webber time. It
seemed to him that After Webber the color of life
began to be different. In this time A. W., the world
came in. Not only the look of things, but his whole
sense of temporal events—his sense of time, the way he
felt about the world—began to change. Seen in this
perspective, the time B. W. had a curiously lost and
lonely look, like the memory of a cloud shadow floating
on a hill. Perhaps this is to say that, before, he had

been a lost boy in the mountains; now he became a boy thinking of the world.

And because that earlier time—B. W.—is the harder to recapture, we shall begin by trying to describe it.

Sixty years ago, in Edward Joyner's childhood, Libya Hill was little more than a crossroads country village. The population was small, and most of the people had come there fairly recently. The "old settlers" were few in number; there were not many families who had lived in Libya Hill longer than young Edward Joyner's own. There may have been half a dozen other families of similar antiquity—the Blands, the Kennedys, the Duncans, the Owenbys, the McIntyres, and the Sheppertons—they could all be named in a minute.

This is not to say that any of them were really aliens, or, as the saying went, "outsiders." Most of them, even if they were not native to the town, were native to the region. Nine-tenths of them had been born within a radius of forty miles.

During Edward's early boyhood the print of the Civil War was still heavy on the memory of the town. Judge Joyner had been himself a soldier, and while Edward was growing up the boy came to see and know a great many of his father's comrades in the war. They were coming to the house to visit all the time. They liked his father, as most men did, and, in spite of Judge Joyner's instinctive and deep-rooted feeling against war, and his reticence in almost never speaking of his own part in it, he had a deep and quiet affection for these soldiers he had known. His son never heard him say a word that could be construed as criticism of any of them, either as a man or as a soldier. Sometimes other soldiers who had been with him in the war would criticize some General for what they conceived to be a strategic or a critical mistake—Hooker at Chancellorsville, Ewell at Gettysburg, Stuart on his raid through Pennsylvania. Yes! there were even times when the sacred name of Lee himself was mentioned critically, his judgment questioned. In discussions such as these the elder Joyner listened quietly, but took almost no part at all.

His son could remember only one occasion when he did express an active opinion on the conduct of the war. This was once when General Gordon, who was a friend, had been talking about Gettysburg; there was silence for a moment when he finished speaking. Then Judge Robert Joyner turned to him, his square face reddened painfully, and he blurted out: "We could have *had* it! We could have *had* it!" Then he turned away and muttered: "The whole truth is we didn't really *want* it! . . . We didn't really *want* to win!"

Gordon looked at him for a moment with a startled expression, seemed about to speak, and changed his mind. But this was the only time the boy ever heard his father utter an opinion of any sort about the conduct of the war.

Nevertheless, he heard hundreds of discussions such as these during his boyhood; the soldiers were always coming to the house to visit his father. At one time or another, a good many of the Generals stayed there: Pettigrew, McLaws, Iverson and Heth, Jenkins, Hood, and John B. Gordon, that generous and gallant soldier who stood in the boy's adoring vision as the ideal of what a man and soldier ought to be. It was a glorious experience for a boy to sit in breathless silence while these brave men talked, to drink the war in to the very limits of idolatry beneath the magic spell of the war's great men. Their talk was meat to him, their talk was drink to him, the sparkling of bright wine to him! He felt the pulse of it, he breathed the glorious air of it, he felt the singing and the joy of it!

It was all sweet smells and sounds and sights . . . with Jubal Early swinging in his saddle on the skirts of Washington. It was all good tastes and glorious war, like perfumes . . . with Stuart's cavalry pounding up the roads of Pennsylvania. It was the lovely smells of smoking flanks and sweating withers, the glorious smells of sweated leather, the smell of worn saddles, the good reek of the cavalry! And it was apple-blossom smell with troops among it; and campfire smells, and brown-coffee smells, and wheatfield smells in Pennsylvania, and cornfield smells in Maryland, and hayloft smells and troopers up and down Virginia, and all the dog-wood and the laurel in the Shenandoah Valley in the spring! And, best of all, it was the acrid battle smells, the smells of gunshot and of powder, the smells of cannon-shot, the sultry thunder of artillery, the smells of cartridges, shrapnel, grapeshot, minnie balls, and can-ister!

When these men talked, he saw it all, he felt it all, he breathed and tasted it all—all of the glory, joy, and fragrance of the war—none of its stench and filth and misery. It was not in the boy's heart to understand the sadness and the sorrow in the talking of the Generals. He never saw the failure and defeat of it, the passionate regret of it, the constant repetition of its bitter and incessant litany of "*Why?*"

Why, they would earnestly demand, had someone left his right flank unprotected, when he should have had sufficient warning of the pressure of Hancock's in-fantry behind the wood? *Why* had someone mistaken a picket fence for a line of soldiers? *Why* had there been a mile's interval between someone's line and his sup-port? *Why* had someone waited from eleven-thirty in the morning until two-thirty in the afternoon to follow up his own advance and effect the total rout of an exhausted enemy? *Why* had someone not instantly taken possession of the hill, when he must have known it was undefended?

Why had Jubal Early, Gordon passionately de-manded, not followed up the rout of Cedar Creek with one single, crushing, and conclusive blow? *Why*, when Hancock's army was in a state of almost total rout, its divisions scattered and its force demoralized, when only a single corps of the whole army was intact — *Why* in God's name had Early failed to give the order for capture and annihilation of that corps, and pounded it to pieces, which a few batteries of artillery could have done? *Why*, when a glorious victory was ours, had he refrained from making it complete, and allowed a vanquished enemy to gather up its shattered forces, and so had let a glorious victory be turned to terrible defeat?

Embattled "*Why?*" and wildly-longing "*If*"—the two great dirges of defeated men! *If* someone had not acted as he had; *If* someone had not gone where he had gone, or stayed where he had stayed; *If* someone had only seen what others saw, believed what others told him, known what others knew; *If* only someone hadn't waited, or had done at once what others would have done without delay—"Yes, *If*," as Zachariah Joyner said with bitter irony, "*If* only men were gods instead of children; *If* they were seers and prophets gifted with prevision and foresight; *If* battlefields were checkerboards of logic instead of fields of chance; *If* someone had not been just what he was at the place and moment where he was—in short, *If* flesh were not flesh, and brain not brain, and man's nature, feeling, thought, and error not the things they are—then there would never be defeats and victory, there would be faultless logic, but no war!"

As for the boy, he saw the thrill of it, he saw the glory of it; he never saw the defeated hopes and passionate regrets of it, in these earnest conversations of the Generals. For, no matter what their sorrow, how deep and unassuaged their resignation, the Generals were grand men. Inhuman war had fostered in them all a wise and deep humanity; fatherless death upon the battlefield, a kind of deep and powerful paternity; awful responsibility, a calm and unperturbed serenity, a total fearlessness of death or life, a tenderness toward man and child, and to all living. He heard them talk of another's error, and confess their own. He heard them question another's judgment, not his courage. He heard them engage in hot debate and open criticism, but there was no recrimination. They were good men, the Generals. They were not jealous, vengeful, petty, mean, and bitter people; theirs was the grief of grief, the sorrow of irrevocable loss; theirs was the sadness for the shattered past, all of the lost joy and the singing—but there was no hate.

And to the boy it seemed a good life that they lived then—sixty years ago. He saw and heard them talk, he listened breathlessly to everything they had to say, he devoured every scrap that they had written—memoirs, reminiscences, autobiographies, personal experiences in the war, as well as complex and highly technical discussions about battles and campaigns, errors in strategy, technical maneuvers. As a result of it, his studies in school suffered disastrously. His grammar was a thing of shreds and patches, his algebra was worse than negligible. To his father's blunt and frequently outspoken disgust, he was deep in "flanking operations" of all sorts, and a "covering movement" held no terrors for him. He had small Latin, and less Greek, but his knowledge of his rear, his wings, his right, his left, his center, and the position of his supporting columns was encyclopædic and profound.

He was, as he admitted in his later years, obsessed. He would go for days at a time completely lost to all around him, sunk in a whole dream-world of war, a war in which *he* played the conspicuous part, a war exclusively concerned with *his* tactics, *his* strategies, *his* battles, *his* campaigns, *his* final and decisive victories—for, since he was a warrior of twelve years, *his* victories were always final and decisive. In all his gory struggles, *he* never lost a battle, or made a technical mistake.

In his mind's eye, and in his war-drunk heart and spirit, he composed entire histories, extraordinary documents woven of a dozen different styles, and cunningly combining the most exciting features in the works of all his literary masters—the cold and dry precisions, the technical analysis of the Northern General Doubleday, the flaming and impulsive rhetoric of John B. Gordon. Like Molière and Shakespeare, the boy took what he wanted where he found it, and, like both his illustrious predecessors, he may sometimes have improved upon his theft:

"The scene upon our left was one of indescribable confusion. Early, unaware of Hancock's movements in the morning, and, through an error of his faulty vision mistakenly assuming that a picket fence somewhat to his right and rear was a supporting column of his own troops, had rashly thrown out his left to the very edges of the wood—when the attack occurred. At this moment, when the Southern line was still resting on its arms, a solid wall of flame and fire burst from the wood. At the same instant, Hancock's right, under the command of Hays, swept out behind the cover of the wood around the flank of Early's unsuspecting line. Under the murderous cross fire of this enfilading movement and the solid frontal wall of Hazard's guns, the whole left crumpled like a piece of paper, and was driven in upon the weakened center. The Union cavalry under Pleasanton now dashed from the woods and drove through the thinned and shattered lines, and the rout was complete.

"It was at just this moment that Lee turned to that young and brilliant officer who, alone of all his Generals, had from the outset of the battle rightly judged the movements through the wood of Hancock's men.

" 'General Joyner,' he said gravely—for he was speaking to none other than the famous Edward Zebulon Joyner, the youngest general officer in the Confederate Army, the commander of the famous Iron-Wall Brigade, a stripling in years and in appearance, but a scarred veteran of battle despite his youth, and in tactical judgment and strategic skill perhaps the superior of any other officer in the whole Army of Virginia—'General Joyner,' said Lee gravely, as he pointed toward the fatal wood, 'do you think that position there is tenable and may be taken by our men?'

"For a moment the young officer was silent. A look of deep sadness and resignation overspread his handsome countenance, for he, better than all others, knew at what fearful cost of men—the men of his own gallant and beloved command—the operation might succeed. He of all men realized the tragic blunder that had been committed—the tragic consequence of Early's obstinate refusal to heed the warnings he had given him that morning—but no matter what he felt or thought, he masked his feelings bravely, his hesitation was only momentary. Looking Lee directly in the eyes, he answered firmly:

" 'Yes, General Lee, I think that the position in the wood *is* tenable and may be held.'

" 'Then, General,' said Lee quietly, 'I have just one other question. Do you think that course the only one that is left us?'

"The young hero's answer came this time without an instant's hesitation, as clear and ringing as a shot:

" 'Sir, I do!'

"Lee was silent for a moment; when he spoke, his voice was very sad.

" 'Then, Sir,' he said, 'you may advance.'

"Without an instant of delay, the young leader gave the order; his veteran troops swept forward, the great attack had begun."

This was the kind of thing, as Edward Joyner later on confessed, to which his fantasy was susceptible in the eighties. He not only thought and dreamed volumes of it in his mind and heart—he actually *wrote* whole reams and packets of it out on paper; and one of the most painful experiences of his life occurred when he came home one afternoon and found his father sitting at his roll-top desk reading a great batch of it. The boy had thought his secret safe, but had very imprudently stuffed the manuscript away in an unused drawer, and the Judge had come upon it unexpectedly while going through his desk to find some letters.

He looked up at his son briefly, very grimly, when he entered; then, without a word of greeting, he went back to his interrupted reading of that damning scrawl, that devastating revelation of his miserable soul.

And Edward sat there wretchedly and watched him, as he read page after page. His father sat at the desk, with his broad back turned on the boy, the late light gleaming on the polished surface of his bald head, with only his thick red neck, the angle of his square red jaw, a small portion of his square red face, exposed. Although the boy could not see the expression of that square red face, he did not have to use much of his imagination to vision its grim intensity. And as Edward sat there, staring wretchedly, he could see that red neck turn a redder hue, the red jaw thickening to an angry purple. Near the end of his perusal, which, like everything he did, was most deliberate and thorough—*horribly* complete, it seemed to the boy, as he watched him read each page slowly and carefully from top to bottom, turning each page face down carefully with a thick and hairy hand when he had finished it—his father began to give utterance to certain harsh, explosive sounds indicative of partial strangulation, and to certain fragmentary expletives which were translatable to his offspring's tortured ears as follows:

" '. . . flanking operations!' . . . Pah!"

And bang! The offending sheet would be thumped down on its miserable face.

" '. . . murderous enfilading fire which drove his whole left back upon his center—which crumpled like a sheet of tissue paper!' . . . What damned rubbish is this anyway?"

Bang! And down went this one on its miserable face.

" '. . . that brilliant and gallant young Commander, the flower of the Confederate cavalry, as he was the pride of their success, whose superb tactical manipulations might alone have served to save the day if only——' "

This, finally, was too much for him! He banged the offending sheet of paper down upon his desk with a tremendous thump, he raised his square red face, and roared out like a bewildered man imploring heaven:

"Great God! Whoever read such Goddamned stuff as this since time began?"

Then he composed himself again, and went back to his reading. Slowly, deliberately, with agonizing thoroughness, he read the whole thing through to the bitter, miserable end. When he had finished, he sat silent for a moment, his thick hands clenched upon the desk, his burly shoulders leaning forward, breathing somewhat slowly and stertorously, like a man trying to think his way through some problem to a laborious conclusion. At last he gathered up the manuscript in his thick fingers, carefully arranged it, put it into the little drawer from which it had come—where the boy had thought it was so safe—and, fumbling in his vest pocket for a small key, locked the drawer. Then he swung around in his old swivel chair, and faced his son grimly and in silence for a moment. And now he took a sheet of paper from his pocket—a sheet which obviously had been crumpled violently in his hand, and at whose telltale and abhorred appearance the boy's heart stopped beating—and, smoothing it out carefully with his big fingers, he presented it to his son:

"Here's your report card. It just came today. Among your other academic victories I notice you got forty-two in history."

Then he got up, still breathing loudly, and limped heavily and slowly from the room.

Edward's father never spoke to him of this humiliating episode again. One of the greatest elements of that blunt, inarticulate, and desperately shy man was his generosity, the warmth and understanding of his essential humanity. His words could be as direct and brutal as a blow of the fist, but once he had spoken, he was done with it; what was past was past, he didn't bear grudges, or try to persuade people to his own judgments or beliefs by the ignoble practices of incessant argument, recessive bickerings.

Nevertheless, he was seriously perturbed by the strength and virulence of the boy's obsession. By the time Edward was fourteen, he was openly and passionately announcing that he was going to West Point if he could get an appointment. Although the father's usual comment on this was a scornful grunt, or a blunt comment that "You'd better be thinking of some means

of earning an honest living and being a useful citizen,"
he was deeply and seriously alarmed. The truth was that
Judge Joyner would rather have had his son choose any
other profession in the world than that of the soldier;
every instinct of his nature, every element of his character, abhorred the whole idea and the life of war.

"It's not a life, anyway," he said. "It's death. It's
true the finest men I ever knew, I knew because I went
to war. But I went to war because I *had* to go—and
that was the reason that the others went. But the reason that you meet fine men in war is because it is fine
men who have to go to war; it is not war that makes
them fine. War is the filthiest, rottenest, corruptest,
and most damnable disease that man and the devil
have invented; and because it is the filthiest, rottenest,
corruptest, and most damnable disease, it brings out
the most heroic and ennobling qualities that men have.
But don't deceive yourself; the reason that war brings
out these qualities is not because war is good, but because war is bad. These qualities come out in men who
go to war because without these qualities men could
not suffer and endure it. Sherman said that war is hell;
well, he was wrong. War is not hell, war is worse than
hell, war is death!"

He was silent for a moment, his square face redden-
ing as he strove to speak:

"To hell with death!" he grunted.

His son pointed out to him, with all the earnestness
and persuasiveness of youth, the advantages of getting
"a good education" at West Point free of charge, and
added that, even though he went to West Point and
got an officer's commission, "I might not even have to
go to war; there might not ever be another war."

"That would be a fine life, wouldn't it?" Judge Joyner said. "If that's all the value you put upon your life,
why don't you just chuck it off the top of Mount
Mitchell and be done with it?"

The boy was troubled and bewildered. "Why? How
do you mean?"

"I mean you'd be doing something just as useful, for

yourself and for your country—and at just a fraction of the expense. No!" he shook his head doggedly. "A peacetime soldier is no good at all. He is a parasite, a fool, and his head is about as useful to him, or to society, as a doorknob. . . . No! You find good men in an army in time of war; in time of peace you find tin soldiers."

He was very scornful of "tin soldiers." No man was ever more generous or fair when he spoke of his own comrades in the war, but, like Zachariah, his contempt for the military pretensions of people such as Theodore was frank and pitiless.

Robert Joyner was especially exasperated to see that the terrible experience of the war had taught so many people nothing. His homely character abhorred romantic flummery. He was an intelligent and experienced observer of men and customs, and perfectly aware of a fatal weakness in the Southern temperament—its capacity for romantic self-deception and mythology. The very root and source of his practical and hopeful character was a spirit that would not yield an atom to defeat. He was the type of man who, had his own house burned down, would have begun to build a new one before the smoking embers had grown cold; and, had he needed them, he would have pulled the very nails out of the smoking embers.

At the moment of Lee's surrender, he undoubtedly had his plans made and knew what work he had to do, and do at once. When he got home, he began immediately to rebuild his life, and from that time on he never faltered at his task—which was, which *always* was, the task before him, the work at hand.

"If there's a job to do," he told his son—"and you will find as you grow older that there always *is* a job to do—for God's sake, lay a-hold of it, and *shove!* Don't shilly-shally, and don't mess around! That's the trouble with so many of us now! It's always been a trouble in the South. I hoped the war would have knocked some of that foolishness out of us, but you can see yourself what has happened, can't you? God knows, before the

war the thing was bad enough—Sir Walter Scott, fake
chivalry, fake lords and ladies, fake ideals of honor, fake
wooden columns on the houses—everything fake except
the plumbing, which wasn't fake because it didn't exist
at all. And now, look at the thing that's happened to
us. I hoped the war would have knocked all that rubbish into a cocked hat, that the beating which we had
to take would wake us up, and that when we got home,
we'd start off with a clean slate, make a fresh start.
That's the thing, Ed!" Robert Joyner cried, and smote
his big hand down upon the desk. "*Get really started!*
Don't you realize that that's the thing that ails us in
the South? It's not the war. It's not the war that ruined
us. Most of us," he went on grimly, "were ruined long
before the war! It's all rubbish for most of us to talk of
what we lost, because we had nothing to begin with.
And the real truth of the matter is that we got off on
the wrong foot at the beginning—we made a bad *start!*
Why," cried Robert Joyner earnestly, and brought his
big fist down upon the desk again, "looked at in one
way, that war might have been the best thing that ever
happened to us—if we had only seen it in the proper
light. It gave us the chance to *start off with a clean
slate*—to wipe out that whole fake and shoddy way of
life—and to begin anew!—to get started *right!* And
now just see the thing that's happened!" In his earnestness, he leaned forward and tapped his son on the knee
with one big finger. "For every fake we had before the
war we have ten new ones nowadays, and each of them
is ten times as bad! Some of the people back before the
war *did* have some basis for their pretensions. If they
lived in houses with fake columns, at least some of
them did own such houses; and although their niggers
ate them out of house and home, at least some of them
did own niggers. But look at the kind of people you
meet everywhere today. You have people talking of the
great estates and houses that they lost who were born
in shacks and raised on hog and hominy. You find
people—like Old Looky Thar!" cried Robert Joyner
scornfully, mentioning a local character to whom Zach-

ariah had given this strange name for reasons that shall presently appear. "You find people like Old Looky Thar—who calls himself a 'Major' now, and never even rose up to a corporal's chevrons. Yes! and tells you of all the land and property he owned, and all the niggers that he lost! You've heard him, haven't you?"

" 'No, Suh!' " Zachariah broke in at this point, imitating perfectly the exact tone and quality of Old Looky Thar's high-pitched, cracked, and drawling voice. " 'We wa'nt no common trash. We owned *niggers*, we did!—We had big estates an' great plantations, *we* did! —We were *big* folks in the community, I tell you!— Why, up to the time I was twenty-two, I nevah had to lace up my own shoes. We had *niggers* fo' *that* kind of work!' . . . Shoes!" roared Zachariah, and banged his big hand down. "Why, damn his soul, that old mountain grill was lucky if he ever *saw* a pair of shoes before he was twenty-two years old, much less *own* a pair! And as for niggers, I *know* he never saw a nigger until he came to Libya Hill, just before the war, for he was born and raised on Thumb Toe Creek out in Zebulon, where niggers were unknown. As we all know, the mountain people hated them. And as for great estates and houses—why, Goddamn his lying hide!" yelled Zack. "He was brought up in a lean-to shanty—he was lucky if he had a corncob—and if he went out in the woods, he had to take a stick along to kill the snakes with! There's your fine old Southern gentry—Looky Thar!"

"And it's not the Looky Thars alone, my boy," Judge Robert Joyner went on earnestly. "It's all the people who *might* do something and who never do—the people who sit around on their behinds mourning the loss of something that they never *had*. Did you ever hear the scientist's description of a certain philosopher as a blind man searching in a dark room for a black cat that wasn't *there*?—Well, the South is full of just such people—people who sit around and sit around, mourning the loss of something that they never had, or are better off without—and there's *work* to be done! A whole new world to build, a whole new life, better than anything we ever had before! . . . And . . . we ought to be up and *doing* it. We ought to lay a-hold and shove—there's nothing to delay us. As old Salmon P. Chase said: 'The only way to resumption is to *resume!*'"

"Well," young Edward said, "why are you always poking fun at Uncle Theodore and his school? He *resumed*, didn't he? He started up the school again just as soon as he got back from the war."

"Yes, he did," his father answered, "but you ought not to resume making a fool of yourself. You ought not to resume tin-soldierdom. You ought not to resume turning out little tin soldiers for a world that has need of *men*. You ought not to resume training little tin soldiers for a war that has already been fought! That's like locking the barn door after the horse is stolen."

"An occupation, by the way," Zachariah put in at this point, "in which your Uncle Theodore excels!"

"You ought not to resume the kind of foolishness and fakery and lying that ruined you in the first place," his father went on. "You ought to resume being what God made you for—what you were intended to be."

"What is that?" asked the boy.

His father looked at him a moment with his round blue eyes, his own strangely boyish earnestness.

"A *man!*" he said. "A fellow who doesn't whine about the past or groan about what can't be helped! A fellow who is willing to *work* like a man—and *act* like a man—and—*be* a man!"

"Like who?" asked young Edward pointedly.

"Why—why—" his father breathed heavily, craned his thick red neck, looked around from side to side, and suddenly found his answer—"like John Webber! That's who! There's a *man* for you!" And he thumped his big fist on the desk.

"Well," young Edward said and laughed, "he may be. But some people think he *looks* like a monkey."

"I don't care what they say," the Judge said doggedly. "There's a *man!* He goes ahead and does things. That's the kind of fellow that we need!"

At this moment, as if to remind him that he himself had things to do, the courthouse bell began to ring, and he got up to go.

CHAPTER IX

The Bell Strikes Three

Later, it seemed to Edward Joyner that his whole childhood had been haunted by the ringing of the courthouse bell. It got into almost every memory he had of early youth. It beat wildly, with advancing and receding waves of sound, through stormy autumn days. In the sharp, sweet loveliness of spring, the bloom of April and the green of May, the courthouse bell was also there: it gave a brazen pulse to haunting solitudes of June, getting into the rustling of a leaf, speaking to morning with its wake-o'-day of "Come to court," and jarring the drowsy torpor of the afternoon with "Court again."

It was a rapid and full-throated cry, a fast stroke beating on the heels of sound. Its brazen tongue, its hard and quickening beat, were always just the same, yet never seemed the same. The constant rhythm of its strokes beat through his heart and brain and soul with all the passionate and mad excitements of man's fate and error, and he read into the sound his own imagined meanings.

He never heard it as a boy without a faster beating of the pulse, a sharp, dry tightening of the throat, a numb aerial buoyancy of deep excitement. At morning, shining morning in the spring, it would seem to speak to him of work-a-day, to tell him that the world was up and doing, advancing to the rattling traffics of full noon. In afternoon it spoke with still another tongue,

119

breaking the dull-eyed hush of somnolent repose with
its demand for action. It spoke to bodies drowsing in
the midday warmth, and told them they must rudely
break their languorous siesta. It spoke to stomachs
drugged with heavy food, crammed full of turnip greens
and corn, string beans and pork, hot biscuits and hot
apple pie, and it told them it was time to gird their
swollen loins for labor, that man's will and character
must rise above his belly, that work was doing, and that
night was not yet come.

Again, in morning, it would speak of civil actions, of
men at law and the contentions of a suit. Its tone was
full of writs and summonses, of appearances and plead-
ings. Sometimes its hard, fast tongue would now cry
out: "Appear!"

"Appear, appear, appear, appear, appear, appear, appear!"

Again:

"Your property is mine—is mine—is mine—is mine
—is mine!"

Or, yet again, harsh, peremptory, unyielding, unex-
plained:

"You come to court—to court—to court—to court—
to court—to court!"

Or, more brusque and more commanding still, just:

"Court — court — court — court — court — court
— court!"

In afternoon, the courthouse bell would speak of
much more fatal punishment—of murder on trial, of
death through the heated air, of a dull, slow-witted
mountain wretch who sat there in the box, with a
hundred pairs of greedy eyes upon him, and, still half
unaware of what he did, let out the killer's sudden sob,
itself like blood and choking in the throat, and instantly the sun went blood-smeared in the eyes, with
the feel and taste of blood throughout, upon the sultry
air, upon the tongue and in the mouth, and across the
very visage of the sun itself, with all the brightness of
the day gone out. Then, as the clanging stroke continued, a cloud-shape passed upon the massed green of a

mountain flank, and the gold-bright sun of day returned, and suddenly there were bird-thrumming wood
notes everywhere, swift and secret, bullet-wise within
the wilderness, and the drowsy stitch and drone of
three o'clock through coarse, sweet grasses of the dai-
sied fields, and there beneath his feet the boy beheld
the life-blood of a murdered man soaking quietly down
before him into an unsuspected hand's breadth of familiar earth—all as sudden, swift, and casual as this, all
softly done as the soft thrummings in the wood. And as
the brazen strokes went on, he saw again the prisoner
in the box, all unknowing still of the reason why he did
it, a stunned animal caught in the steel traps of law,
and now, with those hundred pairs of greedy eyes upon
him, the courthouse bell was pounding on the torpor of
hot afternoon the stark imperative of its inflexible command:

"To kill—to kill—to kill—to kill—to kill—to kill!"
And then, dying out upon the heated air, just:
"Kill—kill—kill kill kill kill killkillkill . . . !"

It is doubtful if people of a younger and more urban
generation can realize the way the county courthouse
shaped human life and destiny through all America
some sixty years ago. In Libya Hill the courthouse was
the center of the community, for Libya Hill had been
the county courthouse before it was a town. The town
grew up around the courthouse, made a Square, and
straggled out along the roads that led away to the four
quarters of the earth.

And for the country people round about, the courthouse was even more the center of life and interest
than it was for the townsfolk. The countrymen came
into town to trade and barter, to buy and sell; but
when their work was over, it was always to the courthouse that they turned. When court was being held,
one could always find them here. Here, in the Square
outside, were their mules, their horses, their ox-teams,
and their covered wagons. Here, inside the building,
were their social converse and their criminal life. Here

were their trials, suits, and punishments, their relatives
accused, their friends and enemies acquitted or con-
victed, their drawling talk of rape and lust and murder
—the whole shape and pattern of their life, their look,
their feel, their taste, their smell.

Here was, in sum, the whole framework of America
—the abysmal gap between its preachment and performance, its grain of righteousness and its hill of
wrong. Not only in the voices and the persons of these
country people, these mountaineers who sat and spat
and drawled and loitered on the courthouse steps, but
in the very design and structure of the courthouse building itself did the shape and substance of their life appear. Here in the pseudo-Greek façade with the false
front of its swelling columns, as well as in the high,
square dimensions of the trial courtroom, the judge's
bench, the prisoner's box, the witness stand, the lawyers' table, the railed-off area for participants, the
benches for spectators behind, the crossed flags of the
state and of the nation, the steel engraving of George
Washington—in all these furnishings of office there
was some effort to maintain the pomp of high
authority, the outward symbols of a dignified, impartial
execution of the law. But, alas, the execution of the law
was, like the design and structure of the courthouse
itself, not free from error, and not always sound. The
imposing Doric and Corinthian columns were often
found, upon inspection, to be just lath and brick and
plaster trying to be stone. No matter what pretensions
to a classic austerity the courtroom itself might try to
make, the tall and gloomy-looking windows were generally unwashed. No matter what effect of Attic graces
the fake façade might have upon the slow mind of the
countryman, the wide, dark corridors were full of drafts
and unexpected ventilations, darkness, creaking boards,
squeaking stairways, and the ominous dripping of an
unseen tap.

And the courthouse smell was like the smell of terror,
crime, and justice in America—a certain essence of our
life, a certain sweat out of ourselves, a certain substance

that is ours alone, and unmistakable. What was this smell of courthouse justice in America? What were the smells of terror, law, and crime in this great land? It was a single and yet most high, subtle, and composite stink: made up of many things, yet, like the great union that produced it, one smell and one alone—one and indivisible!

It was—to get down to its basic chemistries—a smell of sweat, tobacco juice, and urine; a smell of sour flesh, feet, clogged urinals, and broken-down latrines. It was, mixed in and subtly interposed with these, a smell of tarry disinfectant, a kind of lime and alum, a strong ammoniac smell. It was a smell of old dark halls and old used floorways, a cool, dark, dank, and musty cellar-smell. It was a smell of old used chairs with creaking bottoms, a smell of sweated woods and grimy surfaces; a smell of rubbed-off arm rests, bench rests, chair rests, of counters, desks, and tables; a smell as if every inch of woodwork in the building had been oiled, stewed, sweated, grimed, and polished by man's flesh.

In addition to all these, it was a smell of rump-worn leathers, a smell of thumb-worn calfskin, yellowed papers, and black ink. It was a smell of brogans, shirt-sleeves, overalls, and sweat and hay and butter. It was a kind of dry, exciting smell of chalk, of starched cuffs that rattled—a smell that went with the incessant rattling of dry papers, the crackling of dry knuckles and parched fingers, the rubbing of dry, chalky hands—a country lawyer smell of starch and broadcloth.

And oh, much more than these—and *all* of these—it was a smell of fascination and of terror, a smell of throbbing pulse and beating heart and the tight and dry constriction of the throat. It was a smell made up of all the hate, the horror, the fear, the chicanery, and the loathing that the world could know; a smell made up of the intolerable anguish of man's nerve and heart and sinew, the sweat and madness of man's perjured soul enmeshed in trickery—a whole huge smell of violence and crime and murder, of shyster villainies and broken faith. And to this high and mountainous stench of error, passion, guilt, graft, and wrong, there was added one small smell of justice, fairness, truth, and hope.

The county courthouse was, in short, America—the wilderness America, the sprawling, huge, chaotic, criminal America. It was murderous America soaked with murdered blood, tortured and purposeless America, savage, blind, and mad America, exploding through its puny laws, its pitiful pretense. It was America with all its almost hopeless hopes, its almost faithless faiths— America with the huge blight on her of her own error, the broken promise of her lost dream and her unachieved desire; and it was America as well with her unspoken prophecies, her unfound language, her unuttered song. And just for all these reasons it was for us all our own America—with all her horror, beauty, tenderness, and terror—with all we know of her that never has been proved, that has never yet been uttered—the only one we know, the only one there is.

Young Edward Joyner's interest in the courthouse and the courthouse bell was a double one: the sound of that great and brazen bell not only punctuated almost every experience of his youth, but it also punctuated almost every memory that he had of his father. Since his father was a judge of the Circuit Court of Appeals, the whole record of the boy's life during this period might have been chronicled in the ringing of the bell. When the bell rang, court was in session and his father was in town; when the bell did not ring, court was not in session, and his father was holding court in some other town.

Moreover, when the bell began to ring, his father was at home; and before the bell had finished ringing he was on his way to court. The ceremony of his going was always the same; his son watched him perform it a thousand times, and it never changed or varied by a fraction. He would get home at one o'clock for lunch— or "dinner" as they called it in those days. He would

eat in a preoccupied silence, speaking rarely, and probably thinking of the case that he was trying at the moment. After dinner, he would go into his office or
"study," stretch himself out on his old leather sofa, and
nap or doze for three-quarters of an hour. His son often
watched him while he took this brief siesta; he slept
with a handkerchief spread out across his face, and with
only the top of his bald head visible. Often, these naps
or dozes produced snores of very formidable proportions, and the big handkerchief would blow up beneath
the blast like a sail that catches a full wind.

But no matter how profound or deep these slumbers
seemed to be, he would always rouse himself at the first
stroke of the courthouse bell, snatch the handkerchief
from his face, and sit bolt upright with an expression
of intense and almost startled surprise on his red face
and in his round blue eyes:

"There's the *bell!*" he would cry, as if this was the
last thing on earth he had expected. Then he would get
up, limp over to his desk, stuff papers, briefs, and documents into his old worn briefcase, jam a battered old
slouch hat upon his head, and limp heavily down the
hall to the sitting room, where young Edward's mother
would be busy at her sewing.

"I'm going now!" he would announce in a tone that
seemed to convey a kind of abrupt and startled warning.
To this his wife would make no answer whatso-
ever, but would continue placidly at her sewing, as if
she had been expecting this surprising information all
the time.

Then Edward's father, after staring at her for a minute in a somewhat puzzled, undecided manner, would
limp off down the hall, pause halfway, limp back to
the open door, and fairly shout:

"I say, *I'm going!*"

"Yes, Robert," his wife would answer placidly, still
busy with her needle. "I heard you."

Whereupon, he would glare at her again, in a surprised and baffled manner, and finally blurt out:

"Is there anything you want from town?"

To which she would say nothing for a moment, but would lift the needle to the light, and, squinting, thread it.

"I say," he shouted, as if he were yelling to someone on top of a mountain, "*is—there—anything—you—want—from—town?*"

"No, Robert," she would presently reply, with the same maddening placidity, "I think not. We have everything we need."

At these words, Edward's father would stare at her fixedly, breathing heavily, with a look of baffled indecision and surprise. Then he would turn abruptly, grunting, "Well, good-bye then," and limp down the hall and down the steps, and heavily and rapidly away across the yard. And the last thing Edward would see of his father until evening would be the sight of his stocky figure, with the battered old brief case underneath his arm, limping away up the straggling street of the little town, while the courthouse bell still beat out its hard and rapid stroke.

Judge Joyner often said that, outside of a battlefield, a courtroom could be the most exciting place on earth, because it provided the greatest opportunity there was for observing life and character. And it seemed to his son that he was right.

When an interesting case was being tried, he sometimes took his son with him. Young Edward saw and heard a great many wonderful and fascinating things, a great many brutal and revolting things, as well. By the time he was fifteen he was not only pretty familiar with courtroom procedure, but he had seen men on trial for their lives. He had watched the thrilling and terrible adventure of pursuit and capture, the cunning effort of the hounds of law to break down evidence, to compel confession, to entrap and snare—the hounds full running, and the fox at bay. And he heard trials for every other thing on earth as well—for theft, assault, and robbery; for blackmail, arson, rape, and petty larceny; for deep-dyed guilt and perjured innocence—all of the passion, guilt, and cunning, all of the humor, love, and faithfulness, all of the filth and ignorance, the triumph and defeat, the pain and the fulfillment, that the earth can know, or of which man's life is capable.

Yes, the courthouse in those days was a wonderful place to observe the drama of man's life and character: not only in the proceedings of the trials themselves, but in the people who attended them—the crowd of "courthouse loafers" that were always hanging round. A good deal of the life of the whole town was here—and if not a good deal of its "character," at least most of its "characters."

Although his father's house on School Street was just a few blocks from the courthouse on the Square—so near, in fact, that he could be in court before the bell had finished with its brazen ringing—in those days they would pass a large part of the town's population in the course of that short journey. Every step of their way was punctuated by greetings, such as "Hello, Judge," or "Good morning, Judge," or "Good afternoon"—and his father's brief, grunted-out replies as he limped along:

" 'Lo, Sam."

"Morning, Jim."

"Day, Tom."

He was a good walker in spite of his limp, and, when in a hurry, he could cover ground fast—so fast, indeed, that the boy had to "stir his stumps" to keep abreast of him.

Arrived at the courthouse, they were greeted by the usual nondescript conglomeration of drawling country-folk, tobacco-chewing mountaineers, and just plain loafers who made the porches, steps, and walls of the old courthouse their club, their prop, their stay, their fixed abode—and almost, it seemed to the boy, their final resting place. Certainly some of them were, in his father's phrase, "as old as God," and had been sitting on the courthouse steps, or leaning against the courthouse walls, longer than most people could remember.

Chief among these ancient sons of leisure—he was, by tacit consent, generally considered chief of them— was the venerable old reprobate who was always referred to, when his back was turned, as "Looky Thar." Zachariah Joyner had given him that title, and it stuck forever after, chiefly because of its exceeding fitness. Looky Thar's real name was Old Man Purtle. Although he called himself Major Purtle, and was generally addressed as "Major" by his familiars, friends, and acquaintances, the title was self-bestowed, and had no other basis in fact or actuality.

Old Looky Thar had been a soldier in the war, and, in addition to the loss of a leg, he had suffered a remarkable injury which had earned for him his irreverent and flippant name. This injury was a *hole* in the roof of his mouth, "big enough to stick your hull fist through," in Looky Thar's own description of its dimensions, the result of an extraordinary shrapnel wound which had miraculously spared his life, but had unfortunately not impaired his powers of speech. He was one of the lewdest, profanest, dirtiest-minded old men that ever lived, and his obscenities were published in a high, cracked falsetto and accompanied by a high, cracked cackle, easily heard by people one hundred yards away.

He was, if anything, prouder of that great hole in his mouth than he was of his wooden leg; he was, in fact, more pleased about it than he would have been over election to the Legion of Honor. That hole in the roof of his mouth not only became the be-all and the sufficient reason for his right to live, it became the be-all for his right to loaf. The hole in the roof of his mouth justified him in everything he said or thought or felt or did, for he apparently believed that it gave to all his acts and utterances a kind of holy and inspired authority, a divine and undebatable correctness. If anyone had the effrontery—was upstart enough—to question any of Looky Thar's opinions (and his opinions were incessant and embraced the universe), whether on history, politics, religion, mathematics, hog raising, peanut growing, or astrology, he might look forward to being promptly, ruthlessly, and utterly subdued—discomfited—annihilated—put in his place at once by the instant and infallible authority of Old Looky Thar's chief "frame of reference"—the huge hole in the roof of his mouth.

It did not matter what the subject was, what the occasion, what the debate; Old Looky Thar might argue black was white, or top was bottom, that the earth was flat instead of round; whatever his position, everything he said or thought—*was right*, because he said it, because a man who had a big hole in the roof of his mouth could never possibly be wrong in anything.

On these occasions, whenever he was questioned or opposed in anything, his whole demeanor would change in the wink of an eye. In spite of his wooden leg he would leap up out of his old split-bottomed chair as quick as a monkey, and so angry that he punctuated almost every word by digging the end of his wooden peg into the earth with vicious emphasis. Then, opening his horrible old mouth so wide that one wondered how he would ever get it closed again, exposing a few old yellow fangs of teeth, he would point a palsied finger at the big hole in his mouth, and, in a high, cracked voice that shook with passion, scream:

"Looky thar!"

"I know, Major, but——"

"*You* know!" Old Looky Thar would sneer. "Whut do *you* know, sir?—a miserable little upstart that don't know *nothin'* tryin' to talk back to a man that went all through the Wah an' come out of it with *this!* Looky thar!"

And, stretching his mouth open until one could hear his jaws crack, he would point a trembling finger at the all-embracing hole again.

"I know, Major— I can see that hole all right. But the argument was whether the earth was round or flat, and *I* say it's round!"

"*You* say it's round!" sneered Looky Thar. "Whut do *you* know about it, sir? How do *you* know whether it's round or flat—a little two-by-fo' snotnose like *you* that ain't *been* nowhere, an' ain't *seen* nothin' yet! *You* —talkin' back to a man that's fit all up an' down Virginy an' that's got a hole in the roof of his mouth big enough to stick your hull fist through! Looky thar!"

And once more he would dig viciously into the earth with his wooden peg, crack his jaws wide open, and point to the all-justifying hole with a palsied but triumphant hand.

If not opposed in any way, Old Looky Thar was amiable enough, and would talk endlessly and incessantly to anyone within hearing distance who might have leisure or the inclination to listen to unending anecdotes about his experiences in war, in peace, with horses, liquor, niggers, men, and women—especially with women. His alleged relations with the female sex were lecherously recounted in a high, cracked voice, punctuated by bursts of bawdry, all audible a hundred yards away.

Judge Robert Joyner loathed him. Looky Thar represented everything he hated most—shiftlessness, ignorance, filth, lechery, and professional veteranism. But hate, loathing, anger, or contempt were not sufficient to prevail over Old Looky Thar; he was a curse, a burden, and a cause of untold agony, but he was there in his split-bottomed seat against the courthouse porch, and there to stay—a burden to be suffered and endured.

Every time Judge Joyner went to court, he always glanced up quickly as he came up the courthouse steps to see if Looky Thar was there—as if he hoped some merciful act of Providence had taken him away. But Looky Thar was always there. Fire, famine, floods, and pestilence could devastate the earth—but Looky Thar remained. He could always be heard endlessly relating his war experiences to the courthouse loafers. And as the Judge limped up the steps, and the loafers would obsequiously and with scrambling haste remove their sprawling, drawling carcasses out of his way, Old Looky Thar was always there to greet young Edward's father. It was a form of greeting which his father especially loathed.

Although Old Looky Thar could pop up from his chair as quick and nimble as a monkey when he was mad, and someone had opposed him, when he greeted the Judge he became the aged and enfeebled veteran, crippled from his wounds, but resolved at the cost of no matter how much suffering to make a proper and respectful salutation to his honored chief. If it had not been for the intense embarrassment and angry suffering which this spectacle cost the Judge each time he was compelled to witness and endure it, the absurd show which this old reprobate put on would have been a most amusing one. As it was, it was a remarkable exhibition, even to one who was not familiar with the hypocrisy behind it.

At Judge Joyner's approach, Old Looky Thar—who would have been regaling his tobacco-chewing audience with tall tales of "how we fit 'em up and down Virginy"—would cease talking suddenly, tilt his chair forward to the ground, place his palsied hands upon the arms of the chair, and claw frantically and futilely at the floor with his wooden stump, all the time grunting, groaning, and almost sobbing for breath, like a man at the last gasp of his strength, but resolved to do or die at any cost. Then he would pause, and, still panting heavily for breath, would gasp out in a voice mealy with hypocrisy and assumed humility:

"Boys, I'm shamed to have to ask fer help, but I'm afraid I got to! Here comes the Judge an' I *got* to get up on my feet. Will one of you fellers lend a hand?"

Of course a dozen sympathetic hands were instantly available to pull and hoist Old Looky Thar erect. He would stagger about drunkenly and claw frantically at the floor with his wooden leg in an effort to get his balance, catch hold of numerous shoulders to steady himself, and then, with a magnificent show of concentrated purpose, he would bring his arm up slowly to the salute. It was the most florid salute imaginable, the salute of a veteran of the Old Guard acknowledging the presence of the Emperor at Waterloo.

There were times when young Edward was afraid his father was going to strangle the brave veteran. The elder Joyner's face would redden to the hue of a large and very ripe tomato, the veins of his neck and forehead would swell up like whipcording, his big fingers would work convulsively for a moment into his palms while he glared at Looky Thar; then, without a word, he would turn and limp away into the courthouse.

To his son, however, he would unburden himself of his feelings, which, though briefly expressed, were violent and explosive.

"There's one of your famous veterans," he growled. "Four years in war, and he'll spend the next forty years on his hind end! There's a fine old veteran for you!"

"Yes, father," the boy protested, "but the man *has* got a wooden leg."

His father stopped abruptly and faced him, his square face reddened painfully as he fixed his son with the earnest, boyish look of his blue eyes.

"Listen to me, my boy," he said very quietly, and tapped him on the shoulder with a peculiar and extraordinarily intense gesture of conviction. "Listen to me. His wooden leg has nothing to do with it. He is simply a product of war, an example of what war does to eight men out of ten. Don't drag his wooden leg into it. If you do, it will blind you with false pity and you'll never be able to see the thing straight. Then you'll be as big a sentimental fool as he is."

Young Edward stared at him, too astonished to say anything, and not knowing what reply to make to what seemed to him at the moment one of the most meaningless remarks he had ever heard.

"Just remember what I tell you," his father went on, slowly and impressively. "*A wooden leg is no excuse for anything.*"

Then, his face very red, he turned and limped heavily and rapidly away into his courtroom, leaving his son staring in gape-mouthed astonishment at his broad back, wondering what on earth such an extraordinary statement of opinion could mean.

He was soon to find out.

CHAPTER X

The Lost Day

Young Edward grew up in what the historian has so often called "the dark period of Reconstruction," yet he remembered his boyhood as a happy time.

He had a good life in the eighties. As he looked back upon it later, it seemed to him that their little world, their little town, was full of life and hope and growth. They escaped, almost totally, the kind of apathy and desolation of which a great part of the South was victim.

People did not feel the sadness of the war so much in Libya Hill. As Judge Joyner said, they had not had much to lose before the war, so there was not so much later to regret. The mountain people had never been wealthy. They had not been slave owners. They were a backwoods folk—a small-farm, hunting, hewing, clearing, trapping, and log-cabin sort of people. In many of the mountain counties, Negroes were unknown before the war; many mountaineers had never seen a Negro before the war broke out.

Even in Libya Hill it is doubtful if there were more than half a dozen people who had owned slaves. Old Captain Duncan had had by far the most—some forty or fifty Negroes: he owned a great deal of land and had a sawmill, and he had used them there. The Blands had had a few slaves. Zack Joyner may have had half a dozen, and Robert three. Perhaps there were a few more families scattered here and there who had owned a slave or two apiece, but such families were rare.

Thus, since western Catawba did not belong to the rich cotton- and tobacco-growing, plantation-owning, and slave-holding South, its losses from the war were less than they otherwise would have been. Libya Hill, in fact, was still an undeveloped, almost pioneer community. The wilderness of the Blue Ridge Mountains surrounded it and had cut it off from the main lines of development that had been going on in the other regions of the South. Its growth was still to come.

So, as far as young Edward's own life and that of his immediate family were concerned, the business of living in the eighties was an interesting and hopeful experience. Although they were very far from being rich, their circumstances were a good deal more comfortable and secure than those of most of their neighbors. Edward's father had his judge's salary—a modest one— and a little money coming in from rents. Besides, he owned the old house on School Street, the land on which it stood having been inherited from his father, as well as a place six miles out of town, also a part of old Bear Joyner's holdings. This last was farmed and lived on by a tenant, but the family went there in the summer. All told, they had some three thousand dollars a year to live on, in addition to owning these two places. It was not affluence, but it was a good deal of money in the South in the 1880's.

More important than all this, Judge Joyner, like John Webber, was what was known as "a forward-looking man" (this was probably the real basis for their friendship), and the atmosphere around the house, as around everything with which young Edward's father had to do, was busy, cheerful, and hospitable. Someone was always paying them a visit; someone was always staying with them; someone was always coming or going. This gave to their life a perpetual atmosphere of eager preparation and expectancy, with all the accompanying bustle of arrivals and departures, the joy of greetings and the fond regretfulness of farewells.

And, as we have seen, the town itself was stirring at that time with its first delicious pangs of growth, of bursting from its shell. Edward Joyner, like all the rest, shared the feeling of agreeable excitement and elation, the sense of sparkling things that lay ahead. It was in the air.

As a sign and symbol of their golden future, the railroad was coming up the mountain. People waited for its coming with eagerness and a buoyant impatience. And at last the great day came. The last rail was laid, the last spike driven, and Edward Joyner would never forget the carnival exhilaration of that day in April, 1884, when old Captain Billy Joslin brought his engine, "Puffing Billy," around the bend and down the rails into the station, its brass bell clanging, its whistle tooting, the whole thing festooned with bright bunting, to be welcomed by every man, woman, and child in town with loud cheers and yelling jubilation.

And young Edward, as he stood beside his father and his mother on the platform, did not know it at the time, but he realized later that with that puffing little engine the world came in.

Not long after this event, and only a few months after his father had spoken so mysteriously about Old Looky Thar, the boy was in the study late one after-noon and his nose was buried in a book. He was reading an account of the Battle of Spotsylvania by one of the Generals in Hancock's command who had been present at the fight. He had finished reading a description of the first two movements of that bloody battle— Hancock's charge upon the Confederate position, and the thrilling countercharge of the Confederate troops— and was now reading about the final movement—the hand-to-hand fighting over the earth embankment, a struggle so savage and prolonged that, in the words of this officer, "almost every foot of earth over which they fought was red with blood." Suddenly he came upon this passage:

There have been other battles of the war in which more troops were engaged, the losses greater, the operations carried on in a more extensive scale, but in my own estimation there has been no fighting in modern times that was as savage and destructive as was the hand-to-hand fighting that was waged back and forth over the earth embankment there at Spotsylvania in the final hours of the battle. The men of both armies fought toe to toe; the troops of both sides stood on top of the embankment firing point-blank in the faces of the enemy, getting fresh muskets constantly from their comrades down below. When one man fell, another from below sprang up to take his place. No one was spared, from private soldier up to Captain, from Captain to Brigade Commander. I saw general officers fighting in the thick of it, shoulder to shoulder with the men of their own ranks; among others, I saw Joyner among his gallant mountaineers firing and loading until he was himself shot down and borne away by his own men, his right leg so shattered by a minie ball that amputation was imperative. . . .

Something blurred and passed across the eyes of the boy, and suddenly all of the gold and singing had gone out of the day. He got up and walked out of the study, and down the hallway, holding the book open in his hand. When he got to the sitting room he saw his mother there. She glanced up placidly, then looked at him quickly, startled, and got up, putting her sewing things down upon the table as she rose.

"What is it? What's the matter with you?"

He walked over to her, very steadily, but on legs which felt as light and hollow as a cork.

"This book," he mumbled and held the page up to her, pointing at the place—"this book—read what it says here."

She took it quickly, and read. In a moment she handed it back to him, and her fingers shook a little, but she spoke calmly:

"Well?"

"What the book says—is that father?"

"Yes," she said.

"Then," he said, staring slowly at her and swallowing hard, "does that mean that father——"

And suddenly, he saw that she was crying; she put her arms around his shoulders, as she answered:

"My dear child, your father is so proud, and in some ways a child himself. He wouldn't tell you. He could not bear to have his son think that his father was a cripple."

And all at once the boy remembered what his father had once said to him; and knew what he had meant.

A cripple!

Fifty years and more have passed since then, but every time the memory returned to Robert Joyner's son, the vision blurred, and something tightened in the throat, and the gold and singing passed out of the sun as it did on that lost day in spring, long, long ago.

A cripple—he, a cripple!

He could see the bald head and red face, the stocky figure limping heavily away to court . . . and hear the fast, hard ringing of the bell . . . and remember Looky Thar, the courthouse loafers, and the people passing . . . the trials, the lawyers, and the men accused . . . the soldiers coming to the house . . . the things they talked of and the magic that they brought . . . and his war-young heart boy-drunk with dreams of war and glory . . . the splendid Generals, and his father so unwarlike, as he thought . . . and the unworthiness of his romantic unbelief . . . to see that burly and prosaic figure as it limped away toward court . . . and tried to vision him with Gordon in the Wilderness . . . or charging through the shot-torn fields and woods at Gettysburg . . . or wounded, sinking to his knees at Spotsylvania . . . and failing miserably to see him so; and, boylike, failing to envision how much of madness or of magic even brick-red faces and bald heads may be familiar with . . . down the Valley of Virginia more than seventy years ago.

But a cripple?—No! no cripple. One of the strongest, straightest, plainest, most uncrippled men his son would ever know.

Half a century has gone since then, but when Robert Joyner's son would think of that lost day, it would all come back . . . the memory of each blade, each leaf,

each flower . . . the rustling of each leaf and every
light and shade that came and went against the sun
. . . the dusty Square, the hitching posts, the mules,
the ox-teams, and the horses, the hay-sweet bedding of
the country wagons . . . the courthouse loafers . . .
and Old Looky Thar . . . and Webber's mule teams
trotting across the Square . . . each door that opened
. . . and each gate that slammed . . . and everything that passed throughout the town that day . . .
the women sitting on the latticed porches of their
brothels at the edge of "Niggertown" . . . the whores
respiring in warm afternoon, and certain only of one
thing—that night would come! . . . and all things
known, as well as things unseen, a part of his whole consciousness . . . a little mountain town down South one
afternoon in May some fifty years ago . . . and time
passing like the humming of a bee . . . time passing
like the thrumming in a wood . . . time passing as
cloud shadows pass above the hill-flanks of the mountain meadows, or like the hard, fast pounding of the
courthouse bell. . . .

And now, his father dead, and long since buried,
who limped his way to court and who had been at
Gettysburg . . . another man since dead and buried
with the gorilla arm-length of an ape. . . .

And time still passing . . . passing like a leaf . . .
time passing, fading like a flower . . . time passing
like a river flowing . . . time passing . . . and remembered suddenly, like the forgotten hoof and wheel. . . .

Time passing as men pass who never will come back
again . . . and leaving us, Great God, with only this
. . . knowing that this earth, this time, this life, are
stranger than a dream.

A NOTE ON THOMAS WOLFE

[This essay was written by Thomas Wolfe's editor at Harper & Brothers for the first publication of *The Hills Beyond*. At that time several short stories were included in the same volume. These are now available in a Perennial Library book titled *The Lost Boy*.—The Publisher.]

Thomas Wolfe was thirty-seven years old when he died on September 15, 1938. Nine years before, in 1929, he had published his first book and had been widely acclaimed as one of the most promising writers of his generation. J. B. Priestley has said that he thinks Wolfe must have known his time was short and that that is why he lived and worked so furiously. However this may be, nine years were all he had in which to realize his promise, and during those years he performed creative labors that would have taxed the full life span of most authors.

With the appearance of *The Hills Beyond*, his works stand completed. During his lifetime he published two long novels, *Look Homeward, Angel* (1929) and *Of Time and the River* (1935); a book of more or less unrelated shorter pieces, *From Death to Morning* (1935); and a very revealing little volume about his methods as a writer, *The Story of a Novel* (1936). At his death he left a mountain of unpublished manuscript, conservatively estimated at more than a million words—the equivalent in length of ten or twelve ordinary novels. From this manuscript three posthumous books have been edited, and up to a point they round out the same pattern, vol-

ume for volume, as his previous work. There are the two
long novels, *The Web and the Rock* (1939) and *You
Can't Go Home Again* (1940); and here, in *The Hills
Beyond*, is another book of his shorter writings. Nothing
is lacking to make the parallel perfect except a further
revealing glimpse of his methods as a writer. He surely
would have laid bare his literary secrets if he had lived,
because he was the most open and unsecretive person in
the world; since he died before he could do it, this Note
is designed, insofar as it can, to fill the gap.

Illuminating as is *The Story of a Novel*, much still
remains to be said about Thomas Wolfe's unusual techniques. No one, I think, ever went about the job of
writing as he did. His strengths and his weaknesses, his
brilliant achievements in probing to the roots of human
character and in evoking the sights, sounds, smells, and
very feel of his America, as well as his constant preoccupation with the elusive mysteries of communication
and of form—all were implicit in his methods. He often
said that he never learned anything except by experience,
by trial and error, by finding out for himself. This was
true. He had to do everything the hard way. And it was
as true of his writing habits as of anything else. He had
read many books and articles in which other writers told
how they did it—and he found no help in them for
himself. He would talk interminably with his fellow authors, and would even listen patiently, with a faint half-
hope, when a certain pulp writer he knew would stop by
at his rooms in the old Chelsea Hotel and boast about
how he turned out ten stories and got good money for
them while Tom was struggling to produce one. Afterwards Tom would shake his head sadly, a little wistfully.
It would be wonderful if he had the pulp writer's ability
to bat them out and yet could write *his* kind of thing
instead of the other fellow's pulp. But even while he let
himself be momentarily tormented by visions of this impossible fulfillment, he would shrug and laugh and go
back to work. He had long since learned that there was
nothing even the best of writers could tell him that was
of the slightest use to him. He had to go his own way. In
the end he always came back to that. So he borrowed

nothing from others. First and last, his methods were his very own. He invented them—because he had to.

"I've got too much material," said George Webber in *You Can't Go Home Again* (p. 386). "It keeps backing up on me until sometimes I wonder what in the name of God I'm going to do with it all—how I'm going to find a frame for it, a pattern, a channel, a way to make it flow! . . . The thing I've got to find out is the way!" George Webber had just published his first book when he uttered this despairing cry, and was about to plunge into the jungle depths of Brooklyn to live and work alone until he had found "the way" out of his dilemma. It is hardly necessary to say that the quotation reflected Tom's own state of mind after *Look Homeward, Angel* came out.

Till the day he died he was always as honest in speaking of his uncertainties and self-doubts as he was in affirming what he knew. So it happened that I, his last editor, became the most convenient receptacle during the final year of his life for his long and earnest confidences about the work he had done and was doing, and how he was doing it. Throughout that year I probably saw him more frequently than anyone, and what I have to say here is based in large measure upon the things he told me. Beyond that it became my duty after his death to edit his unpublished manuscript, which, when stacked in one pile, stood breast high from the floor. The better part of three years went into studying and editing it. This was a rare experience, which shed a great deal of new light on Thomas Wolfe's methods. So, although I cannot speak with first-hand knowledge of how he wrote his first three creative books, I think I have a fairly clear idea of how he wrote his last three.

In certain important particulars his point of view had changed as he had grown older and more sure of himself. Before that he had been experimenting and feeling his way along. Right up to the end he was still experimenting, and very importantly I think, but also his previous apprenticeship had taught him many things, leading him to modify some of the practices that had once come most natural to him. This was true even in superficial details.

For example, those famous ledgers in which he wrote the first draft of *Look Homeward, Angel,* and which are so often mentioned in stories about him, had long since been abandoned for everyday use. I never saw him write on anything but ordinary manuscript paper. True, he carried a ledger on his last trip across the country and after his death it was found in his baggage half full of notes and jottings.* But toward the end of his life he wrote in ledgers only when he was traveling, and then merely because they were easy to carry around and keep track of. That is probably why he had adopted them in the first place. They belonged chiefly to his years of youthful wandering and were put aside when his life became more settled.

Again, Tom joked about having written *Of Time and the River* standing up, using the top of a refrigerator as a work table. If this was true, and I do not doubt it, the habit of standing while he wrote is another that he abandoned with his youth. His invariable practice when I knew him was to pace the floor with head thrown back, running his fingers nervously through his disheveled hair as he pondered some scene or character, but the moment he got it straight and the whole thing incandescent within him, he would rush to his table and sit down to capture it on paper.

Such changes in superficial habits may perhaps be regarded as outward symbols of much more important inner changes in his whole approach to his problems as a writer, and it is of these that I wish to speak. This Note is not intended as a critical appraisal of Thomas Wolfe, but as an interpretative statement containing information that may be helpful to those who are better qualified than I to determine his ultimate place in American literature. It should be borne in mind that what I have to say refers almost entirely to his last years. They may have been his most important years. At any rate they represent his final phase, the period of his greatest maturity as an artist.

* These notes were published under the title, "A Western Journey," in the *Virginia Quarterly Review,* summer issue of 1939.

Many critics have observed that the literary style of his posthumous books is often quite different from that of his earlier books. Much of the writing is more objective in tone, its lyricism more restrained. This was first noticeable in the opening half of *The Web and the Rock,* but not in the latter half (for reasons to be explained later). His objectivity was still more apparent in *You Can't Go Home Again* as a whole. It is most striking of all in the title piece of the present volume. What is the explanation of this change? What lay behind it? What does it indicate about Wolfe's growth as an artist?

These questions can best be answered by telling what I know of his purposes and of the techniques he used to achieve them. Of course there is nothing mysterious about the ends which his writing was meant to serve. The motives which drove him to write, and which lent such singular integrity to everything he wrote, can be read clearly enough in his books. But his techniques are more obscure, and often cannot be derived from the evidence that is visible in his printed pages. His methods were certainly unusual, if not unique in literature. Very few people know anything about them. Perhaps that is one reason why there are so many misconceptions about Thomas Wolfe.

For example, some of his readers seem to think that when Tom was in the throes of composition, all he had to do was to open the sluice gates and the words tumbled forth in an irresistible torrent like the surge of pent-up waters suddenly released. True, he wrote like one possessed. His first drafts were always done in longhand with a pencil, and when he had a secretary, as he did throughout his last year, one of her chores was to keep a dozen pencils sharpened and ready for his need. With amazing speed he would fill innumerable sheets of paper with his vigorous scrawl, and toss them aside to fall on the floor for his secretary to pick up, put in order, and transcribe. He never hesitated for a word: the words came too fast for him, and in his effort to keep up with them he would often form only the first letter and the last with a wriggle between, so that only the initiated could decode his sentences.

But the analogy by which this process has been compared to the opening of sluice gates becomes very misleading if left without qualification. To understand what was happening with Tom when he was writing, one needs to remember all the years through which his experience and observation had slowly accumulated. One also needs to be reminded of his acute self-tortures of thought and feeling about everything he had experienced and observed. He could not put anything that had happened to him out of his consciousness until he had rehearsed it in memory a thousand times, going back over it again and again in every detail until he had got at the core of it and had extracted the last shred of meaning out of it on every level. One needs to be told, too, of his ingenious experiments with different ways of saying what he wanted to say, sometimes only worked out in his head, sometimes roughly sketched on paper. All of this preceded the moment of spate-writing and made it possible.

Beyond this, one needs to know—and the fact may come as a surprise—that Tom had become a tireless reviser and rewriter. Whether this was true of him in his younger days I cannot say, but it was certainly true of him later. Much as he had told me and shown me of what he had been doing in those last years, I was not quite prepared to discover, when I came to deal with the whole manuscript, how vitally essential rewriting had become to his whole method. Far more often than not I found that there would be at least two different versions of the same episode, and sometimes there were as many as four or five versions. There would be a first draft hastily sketched out, then later drafts that filled in the details, and it was fascinating to see how the thing had changed and grown under his hand. When he was dissatisfied with a scene or character he would not, as a rule, simply revise his draft and get it recopied: he would put it aside and rewrite it some different way from start to finish. He would pace the floor over it, and he might dictate the revision straight to the typewriter—then his secretary would have an exhausting day trying to keep up. In editing the manuscript it was very puzzling to

come upon these variant versions because they were not
marked (the pages were frequently out of order and were
not even numbered), and only a careful comparison of
the internal evidence could determine which was the last
draft and the most complete realization of his intentions.

Other misconceptions about Thomas Wolfe lie back
of the often repeated observation that he was an "autobiographical writer." This comment never failed to in-
furiate him. As he said, there are so many different ways
to be autobiographical that the phrase doesn't mean
much. He *was* an "autobiographical writer." Of course.
But that is not to say, as the term might imply, that he
was only a sort of glorified newspaper reporter endowed
with total recall who therefore set down the complete
factual record of everything that had happened to him
from the day of his birth. Such a notion overlooks the
role which imagination played in everything he wrote. It
is true that he drew upon life as he had known it for the
substance of his books. But so, too, has every other
author worthy of the name. "A writer, like everybody
else," as Tom said,* "must use what he has to use. He
can't use something that he hasn't got." When Tom
used what he had, he passed it through the fire of his
creative imagination, and what came out in his books
was something quite different from any mere record,
however straight and complete, of his own life.

But didn't he use autobiography more literally than
most writers? Undoubtedly he did; but that is not the
whole story either. The most literally autobiographical
of his books is *Look Homeward, Angel.* There he wrote
of the life he had known "in a manner of naked direct-
ness and reality that was rather rare in books."† I doubt
if there was a character in it who was not drawn from
someone he had known. Certainly the natives of Asheville recognized the portraits easily enough, and Tom has
told the story of the storm that burst upon him. He
learned a lot from that experience. Among other things
he said he learned that it was all right to write about a

* *You Can't Go Home Again,* p. 326.
† *Ibid.*

horse thief if one wanted to, but that it wasn't necessary
to give his street address and telephone number. But that
was the kind of book his first one was, and because it
was, his readers have probably assumed that the later
books were of exactly the same kind. No doubt parts of
them were, but not all. After a while there began to be
a difference. Tom lived by a peculiar time sense of his
own and it took him longer than most of us require to
get around an experience and over it. Moving in the
ponderous cycles of Wolfean time, he slowly worked out
the lessons he had learned, and began to get away from
his more literal interpretations of his experience. And the
surprising truth is that in the end he got so far from it
that in some notable instances his use of autobiography
differed in no degree from what is commonly called pure
creation.

One of the most satisfyingly real characters in that
whole vital and full-blooded world of Wolfe is Nebraska
Crane, the Cherokee boy who grew up with George
Webber and later became a big-league baseball player. If
Tom never wrote anything but naked autobiography, one
would have to assume that Nebraska is a counterpart of
someone Tom knew as a boy. But not at all. I have asked
the members of Tom's family about this and their answers are clear and conclusive. His mother, his sister,
Mrs. Ralph Wheaton, and his brother Fred—all have
exceptional memories for people who have ever, in even
the remotest way, touched their own lives or family. If
anybody like Nebraska Crane had been Tom's best
friend when he was a boy, they would certainly know it.
But each of them has told me that there was no one
among Tom's childhood acquaintances who could have
sat for the portrait of Nebraska.

Where, then, did this memorable character come
from? The answer is that Tom created him. And how
did he create him? What was the process? It was the
same process that creative writers of a less "autobiographical" turn than Tom have always used—the process
of observing a great many people of a certain type to
find out what makes them tick as they do, and then of
drawing upon these observations to build a character

who is true to the type and yet is not an image of any person who ever lived. Tom loved baseball and baseball players. For years he was always an honored guest at the annual baseball dinner which the big-league players hold in New York after the season is over. After he died his mother found in his coat pocket a ticket to that year's baseball dinner. Tom knew most of the players, liked to be around them, and loved their talk. Out of his intimate knowledge of them—the "feel" of what it is like to be a ball player—he created Nebraska Crane. He wrote first the chapters in *You Can't Go Home Again* which describe the home-run king who is past his prime but still hoping to stay in the game another season or two. Afterwards he went back and wrote the earlier chapters in *The Web and the Rock*, building up out of his imagination the kind of childhood which might have produced Nebraska, and then making him George Webber's best friend—precisely because that was the kind of friend the youthful Tom Wolfe always wanted and never had.

Nebraska Crane is a perfect example of free invention —the kind that many critics had urged Tom to turn his talents to. And Nebraska is not an isolated instance. In the last books there are other characters which illustrate the same line of development toward a more imaginative use of experience or autobiography. One of them is Randy Shepperton, George Webber's Mercutio, who stood by him after his book came out when everybody else turned against him. Though certain external facts of his career were undoubtedly borrowed from real life, I am convinced that in his essential character Randy represents another imaginative projection of the close contemporary—sympathetic, understanding, loyal—whom Tom needed desperately during that trying period of his life but did not have. He did have such a friend in his first editor, but *he* belonged to an older generation, which made it different.

Another example of free creation is Judge Rumford Bland, the evil old blind man who owned that incredible junk shop and used it to exact a pitiless usury from defenseless Negroes. I have satisfied myself that Judge

Rumford Bland, real and terrifying as he is, never existed in the flesh. Tom conjured him up out of his knowledge of many people, and out of his shame and deep feeling about one of the South's most flagrant evils. But where and how did Tom get the initial impetus to create him, as well as the detailed knowledge of the tricks such a man would employ in his usury? Fred Wolfe, Tom's brother, has given me the answer. Their father, at one time in his life, quite innocently and unsuspectingly, bought a small furniture store that turned out to be not at all what it seemed to be; when he discovered what went on there he was outraged and promptly got rid of it. For the rest, it is hardly necessary to point out—at least not to those who have read *Look Homeward, Angel* —that the lineaments of Tom's father are not to be discovered lurking behind the mask of Judge Rumford Bland. Tom built up that sinister character to depict the kind of man who would and could consent to draw his livelihood from such a "business."

Tom had given intense thought to the problems of being an "autobiographical writer," and he knew how many and varied are the uses of autobiography. In a letter to me, written many months before he died, he confirmed the fact that his development was taking the direction which these examples indicate. He called the letter "a statement of purpose," and it was very long. He spoke of the work he had most recently been doing, and referred throughout to "the book," by which he meant the whole manuscript from which the three posthumous volumes were later taken. He wrote:

Here is what the author has in mind:

He intends to use his own experience absolutely—to pour it in, to squeeze it, to get everything out of it that it is worth. He intends for this to be the most objective book that he has ever written, and he also intends, by the same token, for it to be the most autobiographical. . . . Out of his experience he has derived some new characters who are now compacted not so much from specific recollection as from the whole amalgam and consonance of seeing, feeling, thinking, living, and knowing many people. . . .

As the author has told his editor, this book marks not only a turning away from the books he has written in the past, but a genuine spiritual and artistic change. In other words, he feels that he is done with lyrical and identifiable personal autobiography; he is also seeking, and hopes now to obtain, through free creation, a release of his inventive power which the more shackling limitations of identifiable autobiography do not permit.*

This statement of his purpose did not mean that he had applied the new method to the whole of the manuscript. Not at all. By far the greater part of the manuscript was written before he had thought his way through to this conclusion—some of it years before, as I shall show. What he meant was that he had written certain new portions in this freer vein—to see if he could do it, as he later told me—that he was pleased with the experiment, and that henceforth that was the kind of thing he wanted to do.

It is important to remember this in any evaluation of him, because it shows that before he died he had reached a new stage of growth.

One of the commonest misconceptions about Thomas Wolfe is that his work lacked form. In the main this notion has been fostered by "academic" people. (Not all professors have academic minds; neither are all people with academic minds professors.) Their reasoning runs something like this:

Wolfe is supposed to have written novels. A novel is such and such, the definition being derived from a study of literary history. That is to say, Fielding, Dickens, Thackeray, Willa Cather wrote novels; there is a certain common denominator to be found in all their books—a story, with a beginning, a middle, and an end; that then, or something like it, is a novel. Wolfe's books are

---

* This letter illustrates an amusing characteristic of Southern manners. Tom and I, being both from the South, began our close relationship on a plane of very correct formality, Mistering each other about a month before we felt we were well enough acquainted to use first names with propriety. It was during this time that he wrote the letter: hence the odd formality of its third person singular.

not like that. Ergo, they are not novels. So what in the name of God are they?

Tom had very little to say to those who believe they can understand a work of art by tying it up in a neat little packet, pasting a label on it, and tucking it away in a pigeonhole. He did not write for them and was totally uninterested in them except as bizarre specimens of the human race, fascinating to study but unprofitable to listen to. He did not know whether anything he had written was a novel, or whether it was something else the name of which had not yet been invented. If pressed for an answer he might have said that the second designation fitted rather better than the first. But really he didn't care. The question just didn't interest him. It seemed irrelevant. Questions that did interest him—and he was passionately concerned about them—were whether his writing was good, honest, straight, and true; whether it said what he wanted it to say; whether his readers would understand it as he meant it; and whether they would be moved by it and finish it saying to themselves: "Yes, that is the way life is." He did not know what more could be asked of any book.

Occasionally he might refer to his books as novels, as in *The Story of a Novel*, but it was unusual for him to do so. More often he spoke of them simply as books. So too, he never, as far as I can recall, spoke of himself as a "novelist." In his account in *Who's Who* he said he was an "author." That, or "writer," was the word he always used. The point may seem unimportant, but it touches the whole problem of form in Thomas Wolfe. For if one tries to judge his work by the conventional standards of the novel as we have always known it, defined however it may be, one is licked at the start. Not only will one not find that kind of form in most of his books, but in searching for it one may fail to see the special kinds of form which his writing does have.

His books have none of the usual artificialities of plot. His characters are never manipulated and molded to his own wishes. They do not live happily forever afterwards, neither do they fall into wells or otherwise conveniently dispose of themselves when he is done with them. They

have a way of just living on from book to book, going
about their daily affairs as usual, or else of dying very
much as they lived or dropping out of sight and being
forgotten. That is exactly how things happen in real life,
but academic minds insist that an artist should improve
on life. They like an author to bring his threads together
in the end and tie them up in a neat knot, thus giving
answers to the problems he has raised. Thomas Wolfe
had no specious solutions to offer. He had the curious
notion, shared by James Joyce and many another great
writer, that it wasn't his responsibility to provide pat answers which life itself has not provided.

He was deeply involved with life, and that fact is what
gave the true shape to his writing. For it has a natural
form, an elemental form, the vital form of which all
other forms are but variations on a theme—the form of
life itself. Tom believed with all his soul that the most
that could be expected of a writer, or of any artist for
that matter, was that he observe life closely and see it as
it really is—not just the surface, but the inner reality as
well—and then that he depict it in all its lights and
shadows just as he sees it, and do it so faithfully, in such
exact colors, that even those of us who go from cradle to
grave half-blind (which means most of us) cannot fail to
see it also.

Perhaps some may think that this creed has as much
of the scientist as of the artist in it, but such verbal dis-
tinctions lose their meaning when we are confronted
with greatness. The true scientist of human nature *is* the
artist. He is the only one whose vision takes in the whole
man.

Thomas Wolfe was both scientist and artist. Like a
scientist he was forever making notes to record his observations. "A Western Journey," previously mentioned,
was just such a series of more or less factual notes. Like
a painter, he also kept a sketchbook, combining and re-
combining his observations again and again in order to
test out his powers of realizing "the exactitudes" of his
vision. Just as a painter might sketch a dozen arms in
order to catch the precise curve of an elbow, so Tom
might write a dozen descriptions of the rusty elevated

156   *The Hills Beyond*

structure on Third Avenue before he got the "feel" of it just right. He described the process thus:

> In his effort to explore his experience, to extract the whole, essential truth of it, and to find a way to write about it, he sought to recapture every particle of the life he knew down to its minutest details. He spent weeks and months trying to put down on paper the exactitudes of countless fragments—what he called, "the dry, caked colors of America"—how the entrance to a subway looked, the design and webbing of the elevated structure, the look and feel of an iron rail, the particular shade of rusty green with which so many things are painted in America. Then he tried to pin down the foggy color of the brick of which so much of London is constructed, the look of an English doorway, of a French window, of the roofs and chimney pots of Paris, of a whole street in Munich—and each of these foreign things he then examined in contrast to its American equivalent.*

Those are not the words of a man who was indifferent to form. They are the words of one who was so intensely concerned about it that he labored to achieve it with the most studied and exacting patience. No wonder that his writing captured so much of life.

That, then, is one kind of form he had. But there are other kinds as well.

His inner eye was fixed upon the form of every line he wrote. If you wish to test this statement, try the experiment of cutting one of his sentences. Pick, if you like, some long-winded sentence that is repetitive and full of adjectives. Strike out everything you think redundant and superfluous, and then read aloud what you have left, which represents your improvement on Wolfe. If you have an ear for music, ten to one it will set your teeth on edge. By just a little injudicious tampering, those sonorous sentences which have the majestic swing and roll of mighty music can be reduced to limping dissonance.

But what about his repetitions and his verbosity? He often used the same word a dozen times in one paragraph

* *You Can't Go Home Again*, p. 412.

and strung ten adjectives together where anybody else would have been content with three. Tom was well aware of these faults and was trying hard to control the thing in himself which made him commit them. And he *was* getting it under better control in his last books. When these faults persisted, it was not because he had no sense of form. Rather, it was because his sense of form was too acute and he let it get the better of him. Being a Southerner, with a Southerner's innate love of rhetoric, he would often be swept away by the cadence of his own words. Sometimes, more especially in his younger writing, he attached so much importance to the measured flow of his sentences that he might sacrifice his meaning to his music. Usually one will find that when he repeated a word or phrase, or let himself be hypnotized by the resounding march of his adjectives, he did it for the sake of rhythm.

That is why mere cutting was no solution of the problem. But this is not to say that Wolfe couldn't be cut. His books *were* cut, each one of them, and drastically. Whole chunks and reams of them came out, and they were the better for it. I am only saying that small cutting was often impossible because it would have ruined his style. For the most part he had to be cut as he wrote— in the large.

And it is only when Thomas Wolfe's work is viewed in the large that one can begin to see still another kind of form which it possesses. The academic people who scrutinized his individual books for traces of classical form may find something that resembles it if they will consider all the books together. Taken as one unit, they tell a single story—the story of Eugene Gant who, midway along, changes to George Webber. (Tom thought he had good reasons for this shift, and I shall later tell what they were.) In its main outline this story has a beginning, a middle, and an end. Indeed, if one is a stickler for pure form, it can be thought of as describing a circle, swinging round from *Look Homeward, Angel*, with which it begins, to *You Can't Go Home Again* with which it ends. These are the two hemispheres of his world.

This cohesive unity which binds together the whole of Thomas Wolfe becomes clearer now that *The Hills Beyond* completes the picture. Anyone who reads all the books will see that they are not separate entities, not "books" in the usual sense. Tom really wrote only one book, and that runs to some 4,000 printed pages comprising the total of his works. The individual titles that bear his name are only so many numbered volumes of this master book. The parts should be thought of as having been brought out separately merely for convenience.

The unity of his rich tapestry of life is one of the most extraordinary literary achievements I know of. It is like Joyce in that, with the advantage of being easily understandable. And his achievement appears the more remarkable when one considers the amount of experimentation that went into Wolfe's writing, the changes his point of view underwent from time to time, and the seemingly haphazard plan he followed as he carried his work along.

It is strange but true that not one of his creative books was written as the volume it ultimately turned out to be. *Look Homeward, Angel* came closest to it. Tom said that that book "almost wrote itself," by which he meant that its line of movement was clear to him from the start, and that he wrote it fairly easily, without even being aware of many of the problems that were to arise to plague him in the preparation of the later books. Even so, however, Maxwell E. Perkins of Scribner's, Tom's first editor, tells me that a large section at the beginning of the manuscript of *Look Homeward, Angel* was cut out, since it covered at length the early life of old Gant, and lacked the feeling of instant warmth and reality which came into Tom's writing as soon as the story moved on to Eugene and his immediate family background. The later books did not "write themselves" in any sense of the word, and were not planned as individual books. *The Story of a Novel* confirms this fact about *Of Time and the River*, and the same thing holds for the posthumous books. Tom always spoke of the

whole mass of manuscript from which those later volumes were taken simply as "the book." He did not know
whether in the end it would make one book or a dozen,
and he didn't much care. That seemed to him the publisher's problem, and he was right about it. What went
into each volume was largely a matter of convenience
and practicability.

This may seem to contradict what I have said about
form in Wolfe's writing, but there is no real contradiction. For, although Tom did not plan the various parts
of his story as the published books which we know, he
did plan the parts in themselves, and planned each part
in relation to all the other parts. What is more, he
planned the whole from first to last, and the whole was
complete within him before he ever began to write. Not
that he could at that time have given anyone an exact
blueprint of the books that were to come. His knowledge
was more fundamental than that, much more central to
his purpose. He knew what kind of books he was going to
write, he knew what they were to be about, and he knew
precisely what effect he wanted them to have on his
readers.

These statements demand proof, and I am fortunate
to be able to give it in a form that will be much more
convincing than any report I might make of conversations with Tom or any deductions I might offer from my
study of the manuscript. In April 1923 Tom wrote a
letter to his mother. At that time he was only twenty-
two years old and still a student in college. He was at
Harvard, studying under Professor Baker in the 47
Workshop. That was the period during which he
thought he wanted to be a playwright, so he conceived
of the work he had set himself to do in terms of plays.
Except for this miscalculation about the medium he
would use, his letter was such an exact prophecy of his
later achievement that it must take rank among the great
documents of literary history. He had just been visiting
Professor Baker at his country place in New Hampshire,
and he spoke of the visit and told of Professor Baker's
faith in him. Then he went on:

I know this now: I am inevitable, I sincerely believe. The only thing that can stop me now is insanity, disease, or death.

The plays I am going to write may not be suited to the tender bellies of old maids, sweet young girls, or Baptist ministers, but they will be true and honest and courageous, and the rest doesn't matter. If my play goes on I want you to be prepared for execrations upon my head. I have stepped on toes right and left—I spared Boston with its nigger-sentimentalists no more than the South, which I love, but which I nevertheless pounded. I am not interested in writing what our pot-bellied members of the Rotary and Kiwanis call a "good show." I want to know life and understand it and interpret it without fear or favor. This, I feel, is a man's work and worthy of a man's dignity. For life is not made up of sugary, sticky, sickening Edgar A. Guest sentimentality; it is not made up of dishonest optimism. God is *not* always in His Heaven, all is *not* always right with the world. It is not all bad, but it is not all good; it is not all ugly, but it is not all beautiful; it is life, life, life—the only thing that matters. It is savage, cruel, kind, noble, passionate, generous, stupid, ugly, beautiful, painful, joyous—it is all these and more—and it's all these I want to know, and BY GOD I shall, though they crucify me for it. I will go to the end of the earth to find it, to understand it. I will know this country when I am through as I know the palm of my hand, and I will put it on paper and make it true and beautiful.

I will step on toes. I will not hesitate to say what I think of those people who shout "Progress, Progress, Progress"—when what they mean is more Ford automobiles, more Rotary Clubs, more Baptist Ladies Social Unions. I shall say that "Greater Asheville" does not necessarily mean "100,000 by 1930," that we are not necessarily four times as civilized as our grandfathers because we go four times as fast in automobiles, because our buildings are four times as tall. What I shall try to get into their dusty, little pint-measure minds is that a full belly, a good automobile, paved streets, and more, does not make them one whit better or finer—that there is beauty in this world—beauty even in this wilderness of ugliness and provincialism that is at present our country, beauty and spirit which will make us men instead of cheap Board of Trade Boosters and blatant pamphleteers.

I shall try to impress upon their little craniums that one does not have to be a "highbrow" or "queer" or "impractical" to know these things, to love them, and to realize they are our common heritage—there for us all to possess and make a part of us. In the name of God, let us learn to be men, not monkeys.

When I speak of beauty I do not mean a movie close-up where Susie and Johnny meet at the end and clinch and all the gum-chewing ladies go home thinking husband is not so good a lover as Valentino. That's cheap and vulgar! I mean everything which is lovely, and noble, and true. It does not have to be sweet, it may be bitter; it does not have to be joyous, it may be sad.

When spring comes I think of a cool, narrow back yard in North Carolina, with green, damp earth, and cherry trees in blossom. I think of a skinny little boy at the top of one of those trees, with the fragrant blooms about him, with the tang of the sap in his nose, looking out on a world of back yards, and building his castles in Spain. That's beauty!—that's romance. I think of an old man in the grip of a terrible disease, who thought he was afraid to die, but who died like a warrior in an epic poem. That's beauty. I think of a boy of twenty-six years heaving his life away, and gasping to regain it, I think of the frightened glare in his eyes and the way he seizes my hands, and cries, "What have you come home for?"—I think of the lie that trembles in my throat, I think of a woman who sits with a face as white and set as if cut from marble, and whose fingers cannot be unclasped from his hand.

And the boy of eighteen sees and knows for the first time that more than a son is dying, that part of a mother is being buried before her—life in death—that something which she nursed and loved, something out of her blood, out of her life, is taken away. It's terrible but it's beautiful.

I think of the devotion of a woman of frail physique to a father, I think of the daisy meadows on the way to Craggy Mountain, of the birch forests of New Hampshire, of the Mississippi River at Memphis—of all of which I have been a part—and I know there is nothing so commonplace, so dull, that is not touched with nobility and dignity.

And I intend to wreak out my soul on people and express

it all. This is what my life means to me: I am at the mercy of this thing and I will do it or die.

I never forget: I have never forgotten, I have tried to make myself conscious of the whole of my life since first the baby in the basket became conscious of the warm sunlight on the porch, and saw his sister go up the hill to the girls' school on the corner (the first thing I remember).

Slowly out of the world of infant darkness things take shape: the big terrifying faces become familiar—I recognize my father by his bristly moustache. Then the animal books, which I memorize before I can read, and recite for the benefit of admiring neighbors, every night, holding my book upside-down. I become conscious of Santa Claus and send scrawls up the chimney. Then St. Louis. A flight of stairs at the Cincinnati railroad station—which must be gone up—the World's Fair, the Ferris Wheel, Grover at the Inside Inn, the Delmar Gardens where you let me taste beer which I spit out, a ride on a bus-automobile over the Fair Grounds with Effie—it is raining, raining—the Cascades in the rain—a ride in the scenic railway—scared at the darkness and the hideous faces—eating a peach in the back yard (St. Louis)—I swallowed a fly and am sick—and one of my brothers laughs at me—two little boys who ride tricycles up and down the street—they dress in white and look alike—their father injured or killed in elevator accident (wasn't he?)—I commit a nuisance on the narrow steps of side yard and the policeman sees me and reports me—the smell of tea at the East India House—I'll never forget it—Grover's sickness and death—I am awakened at midnight by Mabel and she says, "Grover's on the cooling board." I don't know what a cooling board is but am anxious to see.

I don't know what death is but have a vague, terrified sensation that something awful has happened—then she takes me in her arms and up the hall—disappointed at the cooling board—it's only a table—the brown mole on his neck—the trip home—visitors in the parlor with condolences—Norah Israel was there—then it gets fairly plain thereafter and I can trace it step by step.

This is why I think I am going to be an artist. The things that really mattered sank in and left their mark—sometimes a peculiar smile—sometimes death—sometimes the smell of dandelions in spring—Once Love.

I will go everywhere and see everything. I will meet all the people I can. I will think all the thoughts, feel all the emotions I am able, and I will write, write, write. . . .

This was six years before *Look Homeward, Angel.* From then on he did write, write, write—and somehow he got it all down. And it is of one piece, for he had the whole thing secure within him.

How, exactly, did he do it? What were his methods? I have said that they were his very own, borrowed from nowhere. If I had known what they were without also knowing what they produced, I would not have believed it possible that anyone could write the way he did and achieve anything but hopeless confusion. They *seemed* so utterly without purpose or direction. But they were not. The purpose was clear in his head right along, and that is why his methods worked.

Studying the mass of his manuscript was something like excavating the site of ancient Troy. One came upon evidences of entire civilizations buried and forgotten at different levels. Some parts of the manuscript had been written as recently as four months before he died; other parts dated back to *Look Homeward, Angel,* and had, in fact, been cut from that book; still other parts had been written in each of the intervening years. The manuscript contained everything that is in the three posthumous volumes and much else besides. There were all the variant versions. There were mere notes and sketches, some of them left unfinished, the writing sometimes broken off in the middle of a sentence. There were fragments that had been cut out of each of the earlier books. There was a long fragment with whole blocks of pages missing from the beginning and middle of it which represented all that was left of the second book Tom wrote —a book called "K 19" which was never published. This was a book about a train. The action began in a Pullman car on an overnight ride between Altamont and New York, with flashbacks that covered the lives of the occupants up to the moment of their meeting. Mr. Perkins and Tom agreed that the book was not good enough to follow *Look Homeward, Angel,* so Tom abandoned it. But he did not throw the manuscript away. He never threw anything away, never lost anything. If he could not use it in one form, he would try to use it in some other, and very often he succeeded. Parts of "K 19," for example, were taken out, condensed, and made into the opening section of *Of Time and the River.* Still other parts were recast and woven into later sections of the same book. But what was left of it was in the mass of manuscript that Tom delivered to me. None of it fitted into the pattern of the posthumous books, so it still remains an unpublished fragment. But an interesting instance of the way in which Tom turned even his seeming failures to account is the fact that he introduced a Pullman car called K 19 in *You Can't Go Home Again* and made it the meeting place of certain characters whose past histories were related. There was no further similarity, but here was the basic idea of the abandoned novel —worked out afresh, and altogether successfully, with wholly different characters.*

As if all this did not make the manuscript complex and confused enough, Tom had changed his point of view a number of times in the writing of different portions of it, and had signified these changes by also changing the names of his characters. When he dropped Eugene Gant he hesitated for months before he finally settled on George Webber. Why did he abandon the Gants and the Pentlands in favor of the Webbers and the Joyners? There were several reasons. First, as he said, he had unwittingly caused his family embarrassment and pain by identifying them too closely with the Gants, and he did not want to subject them to further embarrassment of the same kind. Second, there were many important things about his childhood that he had forgotten to say in *Look Homeward, Angel,* and the only way to say them was in terms of a new character. Finally, he had gradually

---

* There is another interesting and poignant sidelight on this. I was in Baltimore during the final week of Tom's illness and remained there after his death to help his family in making the funeral arrangements. I went to the station with them and saw them off when they left for Asheville. Down at the far end of the platform the long cypress box was loaded into the baggage car. I said good-bye to the family as they took their places in the Asheville Pullman. The train started. As the windows slid slowly past my eyes, I noticed the card in the washroom window. It was K 19.

evolved a more objective attitude toward himself and his work: as he put it, he had stopped being Eugene Gant. He came, as he said, to hate the very name, Eugene, and he wanted a new name to hang out like a flag, proclaiming his emancipation from his former self. In the letter to me previously mentioned, Tom wrote:

The protagonist—the central character . . . —is important now because the author hopes he will be, or illustrate in his own experience, every one of us. . . . The value of the Eugene Gant type of character is his personal and romantic uniqueness, causing conflict with the world around him: in this sense, the Eugene Gant type of character becomes a kind of romantic self-justification, and the greatest weakness of the Eugene Gant type of character lies in this fact. Therefore, it is first of all vitally important to the success of this book that there be no trace of Eugene Gant-iness in the character of the protagonist; and since there is no longer a trace of Eugene Gant-iness in the mind and spirit of the creator, the problem should be a technical one rather than a spiritual or emotional one. This is a book . . . of discovery, hence of union with life; not a book of personal revolt, hence of separation from life. The protagonist becomes significant not as the tragic victim of circumstances, the romantic hero in conflict and revolt against his environment, but as a kind of polar instrument round which the events of life are grouped, by means of which they are touched, explained, and apprehended, by means of which they are seen and ordered.

So Eugene Gant was out. For a while Tom called his new character Joe Doaks. Then he called him George Spangler. Later he gave him the family name of Joyner, only to drop that for Webber when his mind began toying with the symbolism of "The Web and the Rock" as a title, but he retained Joyner as the family name of George Webber's mother. Since the manuscript had been written over a span of years, all these names appeared in it. Eugene Gant was even there in sections that had been written earlier, and the *very* earliest sections in point of writing were in the first person singular, as the whole of *Look Homeward, Angel* originally was.

Confusing as all this seems, the wonderful thing about

the manuscript—the really incredible thing—was that once the extraneous matter was removed, once the unfinished fragments and great chunks of stuff that did not belong in the books were taken out, the parts that remained fell into place and fitted together like the pieces of a jigsaw puzzle. It was simply amazing, but there it was. I discovered, too, that many of the consecutive chapters in *The Web and the Rock* and *You Can't Go Home Again* were not written consecutively. Some of them were written weeks, months, or even years apart. And yet when they were put together, they fitted.

How is this mystery to be explained? The answer lay in Tom's strange plan of writing, the unique system he was forced to invent to meet his unique need.

Since he had the whole conception of his work clear in his mind, he did not have to follow his nose in order to find out where he was going. In the main his chronology was fixed by the order of his experience, so he knew where the parts joined and did not have to write chapters six and seven before he could tackle eight and nine. This left him free to write each day whatever scene he most felt like writing that day. Yesterday he might have been working on something out of the Brooklyn period of his life, but if in the night his mind happened to go back thirty years to some remembered episode of his childhood, he would get up today to work on that, and the Brooklyn material would be laid aside until he felt like returning to it. In this way he might cover within a month various unrelated events and characters widely scattered throughout the time cycle of his story. In this way, too, while writing the individual parts he was also working on the whole thing all the time.

When one entered the front room of his three-room suite at the Chelsea the first thing that met the eye was the incongruous sight of two huge wooden packing cases which always stood in the middle of the floor. These were his bank, his repository for manuscript. When he finished writing anything and had got it typed out, he would salt it away in these boxes. Everything he had was in them, the sketch he had done yesterday together with all the unpublished material that dated back through the years to the very beginning—crisp white sheets fresh from the typewriter mixed in with old manuscript yellowed with the deposits of time and torn and dog-eared by much handling. It looked like a grab-bag, hopeless to disentangle, but he knew what was there and could quickly lay his hands on anything he wanted.

From time to time he would stop his writing for several days and go through the packing cases, taking out certain portions of manuscript and putting them together. If some fragment written six years before belonged with something he had just recently done he would weave them into a single piece, rewriting when necessary. Thus small fragments became integral parts of larger fragments. Then they were salted away again to await the day when they would again be dug out and fitted into still larger continuities. The process was, I imagine, something like that by which mosaics are constructed: first each individual bead or jewel was fashioned; then, when there were enough of them to work with, they were sorted out and put together to form a part of the pattern for which they had been designed.

The mountain of manuscript which Tom turned over to me the day he left New York was not just the ordered parts which he had worked into his pattern. It was the whole mass and accumulation of his writing—everything he had done that was still unpublished. It was the entire workable contents of the packing cases—minus only the earlier notebooks and the carbon copies which he usually had made of everything, and which he retained—minus, too, the non-literary rubbish which he also kept in those boxes and which included pots and pans, old shoes, stacks of letters and receipted bills, discarded hats, useless knickknacks people had given him, a flat iron, in short everything which he had no place for and should have thrown away but for some reason could not bear to part with. Tom gave me the whole manuscript, not because he thought it all belonged in what he called "the book," but because he wanted me to become familiar with every detail of it so that between us we could decide what really did belong in "the book." The rest of it would go back in the packing cases to serve as the nest egg for books that would come later. And once the contents of the next book or books had been agreed upon,

Tom figured that it might take him a year to put that
portion of the manuscript into final shape for the printer.

The next book, of course, was *The Web and the Rock*.
After all the extraneous matter was removed it stood in
the form in which the reader knows it. But Tom wanted
another year to rewrite the second half of it—the love
story—and it is a great pity that he was not able to do
it. In some respects that is the most disappointing of his
major books. It falls into two separate halves which do
not join. Also the halves are written in different styles.
The reason is that the two sections were written years
apart. The first half, down to the point where the love
story begins, is much more objective and restrained. It
represents Wolfe's later writing, after his attitudes had
changed. Having abandoned Eugene Gant, he went back
and re-created a new childhood for George Webber,
working in the things he had forgotten when he wrote
Look Homeward, Angel, as well as a few of the things
that had been cut from that book. For example, the
chapter called "The Butcher" was originally in *Look
Homeward, Angel*. When it was cut out Tom kept it
and recast it. The second half of *The Web and the
Rock*, the love story, dates back to the period of *Of Time
and the River*. Most of it existed in manuscript before
that book was published. It was then intended as the
book to follow *Of Time and the River* and was so announced, under the title of "The October Fair." When
Eugene Gant was dropped, this plan had to be changed.
Tom had never been satisfied with the love story anyhow
and had long intended to rewrite it. He kept putting it
off though, so in the end it was never redone. Tom did
go through it and make certain changes in it, and some
small portions of it were rewritten. Both versions of these
passages were there, and a comparison of them proved
very interesting. What had originally been a complete
defense of Eugene Gant in that tempestuous love affair,
Tom altered in such a way that George Webber was less
tenderly dealt with than Eugene Gant had been, and in
fact took quite a beating from the author. No doubt
this was part of what Tom meant when he said there was
"no longer a trace of Eugene Gant-iness" left in his
mind and spirit.

Following his plan of writing more or less simultaneously over the full spread of his chronicle, Tom had thought and worked his way along to the end of *You Can't Go Home Again*. Whether he saw that as a separate volume I cannot say. He really thought of the entire George Webber story as "The Web and the Rock," with the different parts of it carrying their own subheadings. The first subheading was "The Hills Beyond," another repeated the general title, the last was "You Can't Go Home Again." How the manuscript would have to be divided for publishing convenience and necessity he did not know, nor greatly care. Each volume in the series would turn out to be whatever it had to be, and after it had been blocked out he would knit all the parts of each volume together, fill in the gaps, return to the packing cases whatever did not belong, and the job would be done.

That was the idea, but death intervened. What existed in publishable form had to be brought out as it was or not at all. The love story could not be rewritten by another hand and had to stand as Tom had left it. There were also large gaps here and there in the continuity of the text of both *The Web and the Rock* and *You Can't Go Home Again*. Some of the material that was meant to fill in these gaps had been partially written but left incomplete and unusable. Some of the gaps were bridged by sketchy notes. Others were not bridged at all and were just blanks. Tom had told me what was to go in most of these blanks. He had intended, for example, to write a great deal more about the publishing house of James Rodney & Co., but he wrote very little of it beyond what appears in *You Can't Go Home Again*, and that little was not connected with George Webber's story and was mostly very fragmentary. On the whole, *You Can't Go Home Again* was a more satisfying book than its predecessor. It was much more complex, more nearly finished. It contained more of his latest writing, and even those parts of it that had been written earlier had in many instances been revised and recast in his more objective style. But in both books the gaps remained and somehow had to be filled to provide continuity. So I wrote a few paragraphs as best I could to serve this purpose, drawing upon Tom's own words whenever they were available, and these passages were printed in italics and set on pages by themselves in order to distinguish them from Tom's own text.

Of one thing we can be sure. If he had lived, his final books would have turned out to be somewhat different from what they are. Many sections of the manuscript which had to be altogether eliminated because they were left unfinished would have been completed and put in their proper place. The gaps would have been filled as he had meant to fill them. The love story would have been recast, along with the other material that had been written earlier. And in the end there might have grown out of the manuscript, not three books, but perhaps four, five, or even six.

The present volume represents a very careful selection made from all the manuscript which still remained unpublished after *The Web and the Rock* and *You Can't Go Home Again* were extracted from the mountainous mass Tom gave me. This volume does not by any means include the whole of what was left after those two major operations. That would have been impossible. The object was to select the best, and that only. Mr. Perkins, who as literary executor gave his full cooperation to the undertaking from first to last, agreed with me that that was the thing to do. To regard every word Tom wrote as sacred and to try to publish the entire manuscript, even if that were practicable, would only be a disservice to his memory. Much of it, as I have said, was fragmentary. Some of it represented first-draft material which Tom never meant for publication. Other sections were written so long ago that Tom would not have consented to their preservation in book form without drastic revision. Still other parts were examples of experimental writing that didn't quite come off. These things were all excluded. I can best indicate the selective nature of this volume by saying that if what still remains unpublished *were* brought out, there is enough of it to fill at least three other books as large as this one.

What is left beyond this book will probably go eventually to some college library, and the scholars and Ph.D.

chasers will have a picnic with it. One can already fore-
see the endless stream of theses that will come out of it.

The material presented in this volume has never before appeared in book form. It is published because it
deserves to stand beside the other books of Thomas
Wolfe. Some of his finest short stories are here. Some
of the pieces also have considerable biographical interest. All of them fit somewhere into the single unified
pattern of his work. In the notes below I shall try to
indicate where each of these selections belongs in
Wolfe's scheme of things, shall tell as well as I can when
each was written, and shall add any other interesting information that I happen to possess.

"The Lost Boy." Written early in 1937; it was published in a magazine the same year. Tom used to say that
he wrote a book in order to forget what it was about.
Look Homeward, Angel contains a brief account of
Grover's death. Tom felt later that he had not dealt
adequately with that tragedy, which had occurred when
he was still a mere infant. So he kept thinking about it,
and the result was this fine and moving story. One of its
interesting points is that it illustrates Tom's desire to
extract the whole substance of an experience by getting
at it on four levels at once. Grover, incidentally, and
Ben, who reappears briefly in two later stories in this
volume, were the real names of Tom's twin brothers
who died.

"No Cure for It." From the look of the manuscript,
all yellowed and torn, my guess is that this may have
been written as early as 1929, perhaps soon after *Look
Homeward, Angel* was published. Certainly it belongs to
that book.

It is included here because it is amusing in itself and
because it suggests an interesting literary speculation.
Several people have asked me why Tom gave George
Webber a somewhat misshapen body. The reason is that
Tom wanted George to have a certain spiritual affinity
with himself without being exactly like him in physical
characteristics. Tom was a six-foot-six man in a five-foot-
eight world, and he always said that this fact not only

created obvious difficulties of adjustment for him but also gave him a sharpened perception for viewing the so-called normal standards of the average man. He wanted to endow George Webber with the same qualities. Eugene Gant had been six feet six, so George had to be different. Tom therefore gave him a slightly misshapen body, just enough off scale to remove him from the normal and average without making him grotesque. In the same letter to me that I have previously quoted Tom said of his new central character: "The really important thing—the *truly* autobiographical thing—was the fact of physical variation: to create a figure who would illustrate that variation and all the great human experiences that attend it." But what should this variation be? I suspect that the episode related in this story about Eugene's youth, with the boy at that gangling stage where his arms and legs seemed to be growing at a great rate while the rest of him stood still, may have suggested the solution which Tom hit upon. He simply reversed everything about the gangling young Eugene, giving George a torso that was too large, with legs too short in proportion.

"Gentlemen of the Press." Probably written in 1930 or 1931. It belongs to Wolfe's experimental period, the Brooklyn period as he described it in *You Can't Go Home Again*. That was the time when, after having published his first book, he was testing out new methods of writing and trying everything. For a while he had the idea of writing a book about nighttime in America, and he was going to call it "The Hound of Darkness." Nothing came of it except that Tom later used that title as a subheading in *The Web and the Rock*. The idea itself gradually merged with his other plans and was worked out in various things he wrote in later books. But while he was thinking of it as a separate book in itself he planned to write an entire series of episodes about what goes on in America at night. He believed that Americans are a nighttime people, that there is something in the chemistry of our blood that makes us come more alive at night than in the daytime. He wanted to find out what it was, so he started writing the series and did twelve or thirteen episodes. "Gentlemen of the Press" is one of them, the best of the lot, and the only one represented here.

"A Kinsman of His Blood." Written in 1934 or 1935. It fits, obviously, into *Of Time and the River*. It was either cut from that manuscript or is an example of something Tom had to go back and write when he realized too late that he had left it out of the book in which it belonged.

"Chickamauga." One of the best stories Tom ever wrote, it belongs somewhere in the Pentland background of Eugene Gant, although it was not written until 1937, when the Gants and Pentlands were no more. Tom had gone home to Asheville that spring and he stayed all summer. While he was there he went back into the mountains and met some of his mother's family whom he had never seen before. One of them was an old but very hale and hearty great-uncle—John Pentland of the story. Tom spoke warmly of him afterwards and said that the old man told his story in almost exactly the words in which it appears here.

"Chickamauga" had an amusing publishing history. Shortly before it was written, Tom sold a story to the *Saturday Evening Post*. It was "The Child by Tiger" which later made a chapter in *The Web and the Rock*. The editors of the *Post* had never taken anything of his before, and he was surprised and delighted by the size of their check. He decided that if they wanted his kind of stuff he would not deprive them of it, and that he would rather have their kind of money than only a fourth or a fifth as much from the magazines in which he had been appearing. So with visions of sudden wealth looming pleasantly ahead he had "Chickamauga" dispatched to Philadelphia. He said it came bouncing back in no time at all. He then tried other magazines of large circulation and high pay, with the same result. Afterwards he sent it to his old stand-bys, but they didn't want it either. He went right down the line with it, his visions of wealth shrinking step by step until, as he said, he was at last reduced to taking in his belt another notch each time the manuscript came back. The answer everywhere was the same: the Civil War wasn't timely—we were done with wars! In the end he sent it in desperation to the *Yale Review*, which accepted it at once and paid him one hundred and twenty-five dollars, their standard rate but much less than he usually got elsewhere. He never sold anything else to the *Post*. That one acceptance proved to be just a fluke—a delusion and a snare. With his proceeds from "Chickamauga" he bought himself a good overcoat, which he badly needed, and he always spoke of it fondly as his "*Yale Review* overcoat."

"The Return of the Prodigal." The two parts of this were written at different times—"The Thing Imagined" around 1934, "The Real Thing" in 1937. One interesting point about the two pieces is the contrast they afford between pure imagination and an almost straight factual record. Another is that they contain the germ of *You Can't Go Home Again* on its most literal level. Incidentally, Tom was an eyewitness of the murder which he describes in the second part, and was called to testify at the trial. That whole experience had a profound effect on him. He had been thinking about the law and lawyers for a long time, and now he decided that he wanted some day to write a book about lawyers. He was most amusing when he talked about his various encounters with the legal mind. If he had lived to write that book he would have made the fur fly.

"On Leprechauns." Though this belongs to the George Webber chronicle, it was written in its earliest form around 1931 or 1932 and later revised. As a piece of writing it comes out of Tom's Brooklyn period.

"Portrait of a Literary Critic." The date when this was written is uncertain, but it was sometime after 1935. It belongs to the time span of *You Can't Go Home Again*, that part of it which has to do with the disillusionments of fame.

"The Lion at Morning." Written about 1936, I should judge. In mood and feeling it fits into the pre-depression parts of *You Can't Go Home Again*. It is a superb analysis of character, and illustrates Tom's belief that you can tell best what a person is like by watching him get up in the morning and prepare to go about his day's work. In *You Can't Go Home Again* he applied this same technique in his descriptions of Mr. Jack, of Esther Jack, and of Foxhall Edwards.

"God's Lonely Man." There were several drafts of this. The first, written probably as early as 1930, was entitled "On Loneliness at Twenty-three." Later versions dropped that title, no doubt because Tom realized by then that loneliness was not a phenomenon confined to youth. The essay does not belong to any one period of his career or writing, but rather to his whole life. Written in the first person, it is straight autobiography.

It is a very beautiful and tragic essay, and proves, I think, if further proof is needed beyond his books themselves, that Tom was a deeply religious man in the unconventional and truest sense of the word. Of his profound loneliness, none who knew him well can be in any doubt. But it was at the end a wise and friendly sort of loneliness, a self-contained loneliness, a loneliness that had long since accepted loneliness as the inescapable condition of his life.

During the final period preceding his death these qualities in him were unmistakable. He was working very hard that last year, harder probably than he had ever worked before, harder certainly than I had ever seen anyone else work. In a way I think his work had become a refuge from his loneliness. He rarely went out to see people any more. I doubt if there were more than half a dozen whom he saw with any frequency during that entire year. He saw me once or twice each week because we were working together. He saw regularly Miss Elizabeth Nowell, his agent, for the same reason, and because they were old friends. Beyond that, three or four people now and then—no more, except for casual encounters. He had his work to do, and his time was running out.

His enemy was Time. Or perhaps it was his friend. One never knows for sure.*

* *You Can't Go Home Again*, p. 388.

He would get up in the morning around eleven o'clock, dress, have breakfast, and be at his writing by noon when his secretary came in. From then on he would work steadily for eight, nine, or ten hours. His secretary would do her regular stint and go home, but he would keep on working. Then suddenly, around nine or ten at night, he would realize he was hungry and had had nothing to eat since breakfast, and he would go down Twenty-third Street to Cavanagh's and order a couple of thick steaks. He had a special table at Cavanagh's, at the rear, where he could sit with his back to the wall and watch all the other diners and the waiters. Afterwards he might take a walk, or go back to the Chelsea and stop in at the bar for a talk with the bartender while he had a few beers, or sit there in one of the stalls and listen to the girl with the accordion, calling out to her to play his favorites—some of the popular songs of the vintage of 1912. Later he might drift back into the lobby of the Chelsea and talk a while with the man behind the desk or with the elevator boys or with some of the people who lived in the hotel. When he returned to his rooms he might work some more. By three or four in the morning he would be ready for bed, then seven or eight hours' sleep and up again to repeat the round.

That was the kind of life he lived that year. He stuck closely to his work and let nothing interfere with it. Sometimes I could persuade him to visit me in the country for a week-end, and we would have people in to meet him. He seemed to enjoy the change, but he also seemed to be looking forward to Monday when he could return to town and work again. At such times I would occasionally observe a kind of withdrawn quality about him, as though even when he was having fun some part of his mind was still grinding away at his work. And always, whether he was working or relaxed, alone or the center of a group, the deep and abiding sense of loneliness within him somehow made itself felt. It was most apparent, curiously, when he had other people around him and was holding them in animated talk. As one occasionally finds it in country people, there was something in the quality of his friendliness that suggested the solitude in which he lived—something in the readiness with which he gave himself without reserve; something in his spontaneity, his utter lack of guile, and his willingness to believe that others were as guileless as himself; something in the instant way he could establish a rapport with strangers. I cannot say exactly what it was, yet I believe that loneliness was really at the bottom of it. It was because he was so lonely, and knew others were lonely too, that he wanted to reach out and reassure them, as if to say: "Yes, I know just how it is. We are both suffering from the same complaint."

There had been a time back in his youth when he was not, by many accounts, a particularly friendly sort of person. Because of his size, he had felt that he was peculiar, different from other men, and that people were always making fun of him. He said he went around with a chip on his shoulder, looking for trouble. But he had gotten over that. He had accepted himself, his body, and his world. He had found himself, and thus had realized that he was not different, not set apart or precious in any way. He knew at last that nothing he had ever suffered was unique, outside the common experience of other men. "The whole conviction of my life," as he says in this essay, "now rests upon the belief that loneliness, far from being a rare and curious phenomenon, peculiar to myself and to a few other solitary men, is the central and inevitable fact of human existence."

That conviction, coming to him as it did out of the profoundest depths of his experience, had a lot to do, I believe, with bringing about the great change in him. As a man, it changed him from a suspicious, stand-offish, and unfriendly person to one who was warm, friendly, full of instant sympathy and understanding. As an artist, it changed him, as he said, from a romantic rebel in revolt against life to the brother of all men living and a seeker after more perfect union with life.

"The Hills Beyond." In some respects the title piece of this volume is one of the most interesting things he ever wrote. It is without a doubt his most objective work. In some parts of it the style is lean and bare beyond anything one would have expected to find in Wolfe. There is both a gain and a loss in this—a gain of compactness along with objectivity; a loss of the lyrical and poetic intensity of his earlier writing. (Tom said it was good for a young man to sing, and also good for an older man to want something else so much that he would stop singing.) Moreover, "The Hills Beyond" is a work of almost pure imagination, with only a few traces here and there of factual identity with the history of his own family. Most of it represents the very last work he did. One chapter, "The Bell Strikes Three," was written as early as 1936 and was published in a magazine that year, but the rest of it came later, and was, as I happen to know, the section of manuscript which he had been writing and rewriting just before he died.

The story of how and why he wrote it is particularly interesting.

The fact has been previously mentioned that a large introductory section in the original manuscript of *Look Homeward, Angel* was cut out of that book, and that this cut section covered old Gant's early life before he met and married Eliza. Tom kept these pages, as he kept everything, and at some later time he decided that he would use them in a book that he wanted to write about the Gant and Pentland ancestors. His mother had told him innumerable stories about her family, and if he wrote them all down and combined them in some way with the early Gant material, he would certainly have enough to make a complete book. From time to time he worked at this idea, writing down his mother's stories— stories of the Pentlands—and putting them away for safekeeping in his packing cases. He even thought up the title for the book: he would call it "The Hills Beyond Pentland."

Meanwhile *Look Homeward, Angel* came out and the violent repercussions of its reception unsettled him for some months. When he was able to get back to work the thing he was most interested in doing was to carry forward the story of Eugene Gant. He tried to do that in the abortive "K 19," and put it aside. Then he wrote *Of Time and the River*, and the love story that was intended as its sequel, "The October Fair." "The Hills

Beyond Pentland" was announced as the book to be published after that.

But it was at just this juncture that Tom changed his course and threw the Gants and Pentlands overboard. The many problems of working out what he wanted to do in terms of the Webbers and Joyners engaged all his energies for several years, during which he wrote *The Web and the Rock* and *You Can't Go Home Again*. Gradually "The Hills Beyond Pentland" had slipped into the background and was lost sight of as a book.

But the sections of manuscript he had written for that book were not lost. They had never been lost. They had, in fact, been in pretty constant use. A characteristic thing had happened. At one time or another Tom's packing cases contained all the Pentland stories and all the early Gant material that had been cut from *Look Homeward, Angel*, together with everything else that he wrote as he went along—and all of it was there to be used as he needed it. And he found that he did need the ancestors quite a bit. Eliza Gant, and later Aunt Maw, were always delving back into the past, bringing up some forgotten bit of family history. There seemed to be no end to what those two could remember. Before Tom was quite aware of what was happening, they had managed between them to remember pretty much all of what he had once planned as "The Hills Beyond Pentland." He had scattered it through all the other books.

But Tom did not let go of an idea easily once he had got it fixed in his mind. For years he had meant to do a book about the ancestors, and by God he still would! As soon as *You Can't Go Home Again* was finished, he turned back to the task in earnest. It was not till then, he told me, that he realized how completely he had nibbled away all the Pentlands and Gants. That was too bad, but just the same George Webber, like Eugene, had to have ancestors. There was nothing left to do but invent them. So he did. He started from scratch and wrote "The Hills Beyond." The chapters which are here published under that title bear no resemblance, except in a few unimportant details, to anything Tom ever wrote or intended for "The Hills Beyond Pentland."

I have asked Mrs. Wolfe about the new characters who appear in these pages for the first time. With the exception of old Bill Joyner and perhaps Miss Hattie she can't place them in her family tree. Old Bill belongs there all right, but his sons—Zachariah, Rufus, Theodore, and Robert, and Robert's son Edward—were hatched from cuckoo's eggs. There is some basis in family history, too, she says, for the schism between the Presbyterian and Baptist branches, but the fact was the reverse of the way Tom has it in the story: *his* ancestors were the Presbyterians, while George Webber is represented as coming from the Baptist side. Beyond these similarities, which touch only a small portion of the story, Tom made up the rest of it.

Tom's account of the early Joyners is complete within its own terms, yet it remains unfinished. He was working on it right up to the last, but there was still a lot more he was going to add to it. George Webber's grandfather was Lafayette Joyner, son of old Bill by his second marriage. Lafayette is mentioned in the story, but that is all. How he came to town, how his daughter Amelia met and married John Webber, how the story would have gone on to develop the relationship between the town Joyners and the country Joyners, are questions that remain unanswered. Tom would have answered them if he had lived to complete it. He also intended to make a good deal more of Rufus Joyner and Miss Hattie, both of whom are merely sketched in.

As it stands, "The Hills Beyond" brings the story of the ancestors down to about 1880. *The Web and the Rock* begins with George Webber's birth in 1900. Tom was going to fill this gap of twenty years and make "The Hills Beyond" a complete book in itself. It would then have ended where *The Web and the Rock* begins, thus rounding out the Webber-Joyner cycle.

And time passing . . . passing like a leaf . . . time passing, fading like a flower . . . time passing like a river flowing . . . time passing . . . and remembered suddenly, like the forgotten hoof and wheel . . .

Time passing as men pass who never will come back again

. . . and leaving us, Great God, with only this . . . knowing that this earth, this time, this life, are stranger than a dream.

With these closing words of "The Hills Beyond" the eloquent tongue of Thomas Wolfe is stilled. His books are ended.

They are joyful and hopeful books, and at the same time deeply tragic. And as he pointed out in the essay on "God's Lonely Man," there is no contradiction between those emotions. As one finishes the pages so teeming with the full red blood of life, so pregnant also with awareness of the death that lies in wait for every man, one suddenly remembers with something of the shock of its first impact the three-year-old fact that Thomas Wolfe is dead.

That is the real tragedy—for us. He had just come into the fullness of his powers when he died. What he might yet have written had he lived is now lost to us forever.

EDWARD C. ASWELL

August 1941